F
B11   Babel, Isaak E.
        You must know everything.

Temple Israel
Library
Minneapolis, Minn.

    Please sign your full name on the **above** card.

    Return books promptly to the Library or Temple Office.

    Fines will be charged for overdue books or for damage or loss of same.

I B

ISAAC BABEL

You Must Know Everything

Stories 1915–1937

TRANSLATED FROM THE RUSSIAN BY
MAX HAYWARD

EDITED, AND WITH NOTES, BY
NATHALIE BABEL

FARRAR, STRAUS AND GIROUX

NEW YORK

F
B11

To the memory of

my parents

N.B.

Preface

"No STEEL can pierce the human heart so chillingly as a period at the right moment." All his life the man who wrote this sentence battled painfully with words. Babel's own exacting standards, compounded by ferocious Stalinist censorship, reduced his output to a small body of work. His fame rests mainly on some fifty short stories, most of them collected under the title *Red Cavalry*.

By the time of his arrest in May 1939, Babel had been quite thoroughly "silenced." The circle of repression had narrowed around him to the point of asphyxia. On the one hand, he was under severe official attack for his lack of "production" (a dozen stories and a few journalistic pieces were all he published in the thirties); on the other hand, what he submitted to editors was more often than not judged "unprintable." The few interviews he gave were heavily altered when published, or not published at all. Babel did not protest, but neither did his style "improve" according to the Leninist-Stalinist theories of literature. Instead, Babel chose silence rather than compromise —he wrote for himself.

Whoever entered Babel's study at this time saw shelves piled with manuscripts, but he read them to no one. All these manuscripts were confiscated when he was arrested; even though the Soviet authorities have been only too willing to cooperate in the search for them in recent years, they have never been located. Most probably they were reduced to ashes with the rest of the secret-police archives in December 1941, during the burning that went on for so many days and nights as the Germans were approaching Moscow.

From 1939 until the mid-fifties Babel's name was taboo in the Soviet Union. His contemporaries feared to mention him and for the new generation he did not exist—he had been banished from the schoolbooks and encyclopedias. Since 1957 a slow and uneven process of "rehabilitation" has been under way in Babel's native country. Publication, though infrequent and incomplete, has been resumed and patient digging by a few Babel scholars has yielded a number of stories from the post-revolutionary period, stories that had been published only once, in obscure provincial journals, then forgotten.

One of Babel's idiosyncrasies, whether in Moscow, Leningrad, or Kiev, was to establish a secret place to work. He would usually "hide" in the house of a close friend, to whom he would also entrust copies or variants of his work. Because of this habit a few unpublished stories have survived, thanks to the courage and faith of such friends. As the fear of reprisal has lessened in the last few years, these people have released Babel's old manuscripts for publication.

One rather extraordinary example of such a discovery is the diary Babel kept during the Civil War (at twenty-five, he joined the Red Army as a war correspondent and followed the Cavalry as it drove the Poles from the Ukraine). The entries in this diary are dated from June 3

to September 15, 1920. Pages 69 to 89, covering the period
from June 6 to July 11, are lost. The text, written on horseback, is a sometimes almost indecipherable record of personal observations and reactions; names of places and
people, striking details and associations of ideas alternate
with reminiscences, snatches of conversations, descriptions
of things seen. The unifying thread in this apparent disorder is the repeated injunction to himself to "describe."
This was raw material for further elaboration and, indeed,
the diary was clearly the matrix of the Red Cavalry stories.
Unfortunately, this invaluable source for the study of
Babel's development is not yet available to the public.
Apparently the diary, though now almost fifty years old,
is still considered too controversial to be published in the
Soviet Union except in brief excerpts.

The twenty-five stories in this volume fall into the
following categories:

Stories not yet published in the Soviet Union:
AND THEN THERE WERE NONE
THE JEWESS

Stories first published in the Soviet Union only recently:
YOU MUST KNOW EVERYTHING
SUNSET

*Stories first published in Soviet periodicals during
Babel's lifetime:*
LEAVES FROM MY NOTEBOOK (*four stories*)
SHABOS NAHAMU
DIARY (*six stories*)
OBSERVATIONS ON WAR (*four stories*)

AN EVENING AT THE EMPRESS'S
THE CHINAMAN
BAGRAT-OGLY AND THE EYES OF HIS BULL
GRISHCHUK
A HARD-WORKING WOMAN
SULAK

Max Hayward's translations of all the stories in this book are the first in any language, as far as can be determined. Certain of these translations were originally published in the following magazines: "Shabos Nahamu," in *The Atlantic Monthly;* "The Deserter" and "The Quaker," in *Commentary;* "And Then There Were None," in *Dissent;* "The Public Library," "Mosaic," "The Blind Men," and "Grishchuk," in *Harper's Bazaar;* "You Must Know Everything" and sections I to III of "The Jewess," in *The New Yorker.*

The speech by Ehrenburg and the articles by Nikulin, Munblit, and Paustovsky gathered in the Appendices, together with a Babel interview which had to wait some twenty-seven years to be printed, demonstrate how difficult it has been to ensure that Babel's place in Russian literary history be more fully acknowledged. Most of these texts are connected with the public commemoration held in Moscow on November 11, 1964, in honor of the seventieth anniversary of Babel's birth. This meeting was still very much a topic of conversation when I visited Moscow a few weeks later. At that time it seemed that calling oneself "a friend" of Babel implied not only a renewed pride but also a restless sense of guilt for his death and a wish for absolution. Among Babel's aging contemporaries, this need seemed to be felt with growing urgency. Thus there was relief and a legitimate feeling of accomplishment in the fact that—though they had not been able to help the man—at least they had done what they could to correct the long betrayal of the writer. Read in such a light, I believe that Ilya Ehrenburg's impassioned speech —never before published anywhere—and Konstantin Paustovsky's moving tribute have acquired, since their recent deaths, an all the more significant dimension.

Perhaps one day we shall have Babel's complete works. I regard this new collection of stories as a step toward that end.

An editor's debts are all the more numerous in that his work often seems to demand a kind of omniscience. I wish to express my gratitude to those whose help has made the presentation of this book—as I envisaged it—possible.

I feel it a privilege to have had Max Hayward as translator. His exceptional knowledge of everything Russian, his command of his craft, and the exacting standards he set for himself in the notoriously difficult task of translating Babel provided me with the best English renderings I could have hoped to secure. His numerous editorial suggestions have also proved invaluable.

Professor Robert A. Maguire of Columbia University painstakingly supervised the preparation of this collection. He subjected the manuscript of my notes to a thorough critical examination which led to revisions and improvements at innumerable points. For his generous help and often-needed encouragements I am greatly indebted and thankful.

I also wish to acknowledge Professor Alexander Erlich's assistance in the research for some particularly obscure notes and Professor Serge Gavronsky's help in my translations from the French.

For his reading and criticizing of early drafts, his many stylistic improvements, and his remarkable patience I owe special thanks to Michael di Capua, my editor at Farrar, Straus and Giroux.

The preparation of this book has required of me an unlikely combination of filial devotion and scholarly skills. The persistence and steadiness needed to carry out the project would not have been available without my husband's love. This book is also his.

NATHALIE BABEL

New York
1969

Contents

YOU MUST KNOW EVERYTHING   1

Leaves from My Notebook   13

THE PUBLIC LIBRARY   17

THE NINE   21

ODESSA   26

INSPIRATION   31

SHABOS NAHAMU   35

Diary   47

MOSAIC   53

A FINE INSTITUTION   57

THE BLIND MEN   60

EVACUEES   65

PREMATURE BABIES   68

THE PALACE OF MOTHERHOOD   71

Observations on War   75

ON THE FIELD OF HONOR   81

THE DESERTER   84

xiii

OLD MARESCOT'S FAMILY   87

THE QUAKER   90

AN EVENING AT THE EMPRESS'S   95

THE CHINAMAN   103

BAGRAT-OGLY AND THE EYES OF HIS BULL   111

GRISHCHUK   119

AND THEN THERE WERE NONE   125

SUNSET   135

A HARD-WORKING WOMAN   155

THE JEWESS   163

SULAK   185

Notes on the Stories   193

Appendices   203

BABEL ANSWERS QUESTIONS ABOUT HIS WORK/
   An Interview of September 28, 1937   205

The Moscow Commemoration of Babel's
Seventieth Birthday   223

ILYA EHRENBURG / *A Speech at a Moscow Meeting*
in Honor of Babel, November 11, 1964   229
LEV NIKULIN / *Years of Our Life: Babel, on His*
Seventieth Birthday   239
GEORGY MUNBLIT / *Reminiscences of Babel*   259
KONSTANTIN PAUSTOVSKY / *A Few Words about Babel*   275

I am writing

of things long forgotten

ISAAC BABEL

You Must Know Everything

(1915)

In 1925, when he had not yet completed Red Cavalry, *Babel published the two stories which begin his childhood cycle, "The Story of My Dovecote" and "First Love." Then in 1931 he wrote to his mother: "I asked Katya to send you . . . a copy of the magazine* Young Guard. *In it I make my debut, after several years of silence, with a small extract ["Awakening"] from a book which will have the general title* The Story of My Dovecote. *The subjects of the stories are all taken from my childhood, but, of course, there is much that has been made up and changed. When the book is finished, it will become clear why I had to do all that."* It was during the same year, 1931, that "In the Basement" appeared. "Di Grasso," the last story that can be included in this group, was published in 1937.*

The childhood cycle is looked upon as one of Babel's finest achievements and "You Must Know Everything," his earliest-known work of fiction, belongs to it. This story deals with material familiar from the rest of the cycle: a Jewish boy's excessive schooling, his fascination with literature, and his frustrated longing for "fresh air." In the other stories we are introduced to the boy's father and mother, his Aunt Bobka and

---

* Isaac Babel, *The Lonely Years, 1925–1939: Unpublished Stories and Private Correspondence.* Andrew R. MacAndrew and Max Hayward, trans.; Nathalie Babel, ed. (New York: Farrar, Straus and Giroux, 1964), p. 189.

3

Uncle Simon, and his eccentric grandfather. In this one, Babel gives a portrait of his grandmother and an illustration of how she was educating her grandson, thus completing the description of the schoolboy's world.

"You Must Know Everything" is less complex than the other childhood stories to the extent that it deals with only two characters and one brief span of time, and introduces neither flashbacks nor side plots. Nevertheless, a fusion of inspiration, style, and content has been achieved and one can only wonder at Babel's failure to publish the story.

The handwritten manuscript came to light in the Soviet Union only very recently. It was published for the first time in 1965, in Volume 74 of the distinguished Soviet series Literary Heritage (Literaturnoye nasledstvo). The first page of the manuscript carries simply the heading "Childhood. At Grandmother's" (Detstvo. U Babushki) and the note "Saratov, 12th of November 1915." ("You Must Know Everything" is a line from the story.) Babel was twenty-one at that time and was finishing his work at the Institute of Financial and Business Studies, which had been moved from Kiev to Saratov at the start of the First World War.

The last three lines of the manuscript, written on a separate sheet, are incomplete and garbled and have been omitted from the present translation.

You Must Know Everything

O N SATURDAYS I always came home late, after my six
lessons at school. Walking home through the streets
never seemed to me a waste of time. It was very good for
daydreaming, and everything looked so nice and familiar.
I knew all the signs, the stonework of the houses, the store-
fronts. I knew them in some special way all my own, and
I was quite convinced that I saw in them what really mat-
tered, the mysterious something that we adults call the
"essence of things." It was all very firmly fixed in my mind.
If anybody happened to mention one of the stores, I could
immediately picture its sign, with the gilt letters and the
scratch in the left-hand corner, the girl cashier with her
high hairdo, and the aura clinging to the place, which
was unlike the aura of any other store. And it was from
such stores, people, auras, and theater posters that I pieced
together my native city of Odessa. I remember, feel, and
love it to this very day. I know it as one knows the fragrance of one's mother's skin—the flavor of love, words,
smiles. I love it because I grew up in it, was happy, sad,
and dreamed my dreams—fervent dreams that will never
return.

I always walked along the main street, which was the
most crowded. The Saturday I am going to write about

was at the beginning of spring. At that time of year we didn't have that mild and soft air which, in Central Russia, is so exquisite over some quiet river or gentle valley. We had a slight glinting chill in the air, a hint of passion with a cold edge to it. I was just a kid at the time and knew nothing about anything, but, blossoming and rosy-cheeked, I was affected by the spring just the same. I always took my time on the way home from school. I scrutinized every jewel in the jeweler's shop and read the theater posters from beginning to end. Once I was studying the pale-pink corsets with crinkly garters at Madame Rosalie's and was just about to move on when I bumped into a tall student with a large black mustache. He was grinning all over his face and he said, "Having a good look, eh?" I blushed. He gave me a knowing pat on the back and said condescendingly, "Keep it up, old fellow. Good for you! All the best!" He guffawed, turned on his heel, and walked away. I was very embarrassed, went straight home, and never again stopped to gaze into Madame Rosalie's shopwindow.

I was supposed to spend this particular Saturday at home with my grandmother. She had her own room at the far end of the apartment, behind the kitchen. In the corner of her room there was a stove; Grandmother always felt cold. It was always hot and stuffy in her room, and this made me miserable and I wanted to escape. On this day I took all my paraphernalia—books, music stand, and violin—into Grandmother's room. The table was already laid for me. Grandmother sat in her corner while I ate. Neither of us said a word. The door was shut and we were alone. For dinner I had cold gefilte fish with horseradish —a dish for the sake of which it would pay one to convert to Judaism—a thick, tasty soup, roast meat and onions,

lettuce, fruit salad, coffee, pie, and apples. I ate it all. I
may have been a daydreamer, but I also had an appetite.
Grandmother cleared the table, and the room became
neat and clean. There were some sickly-looking flowers
on the windowsill. The only living things that Grandmother loved were her son, her grandson, her dog Mimi,
and flowers. Mimi also came in, curled up on the sofa,
and immediately fell asleep. She was a terrible sleepyhead
but a wonderful dog—kind, sensible, small, and good-
looking. She was a pug, with a light-colored coat. She had
not grown fat and flabby in her old age but had kept
herself in good trim. She lived out the whole of her life of
fifteen years with us, from birth to death, and, naturally
enough, she loved us all, particularly Grandmother, who
was so hard and merciless. Some other time I will tell the
story of their silent and furtive friendship. It is a good,
moving, and tender story.

Anyway, there we were, all three of us—Grandmother,
Mimi, and I. Mimi was sleeping; Grandmother, in a good
humor, sat in the corner in her silk Sabbath dress; and I
was supposed to do my lessons. It was a difficult day for
me. I had already had six lessons at school, and now my
music teacher, Mr. Sorokin, was supposed to come, and
so was Mr. L., my Hebrew teacher, to give a lesson we
had missed. Peysson, the French teacher, might also come,
and I had to prepare a lesson for him. There would be no
trouble with L.—we were old friends—but music and those
scales were sheer misery!

I spread out my exercise books and began to do my
lessons. Grandmother did not interrupt me—God forbid!
Her face was drawn and blank because of her reverence
for my work. She fastened her round, bright yellow eyes

on me. Whenever I turned over a page, they followed the movement of my hand. Anybody else would have been made very ill at ease by this fixed and ever-watchful gaze, but I had grown used to it. Later she would listen to me rehearse my lessons. She was at home only in Yiddish, and her Russian was very bad—she garbled it in her own peculiar way, using a lot of Polish and Yiddish words. Of course, she couldn't read or write in Russian, and she would hold a Russian book upside down. But this didn't prevent her from going through my lessons with me from beginning to end. She couldn't understand a word, but she listened intently, and the music of the words was sweet to her ears. She was full of reverence for learning, had great faith in me, and wanted me to become a rich man.

When I had finished with the lessons, I did some reading. At that time I was reading Turgenev's "First Love." I liked everything about it—the vivid words, descriptions, and conversations—but that afternoon I was particularly thrilled by the scene in which Vladimir's father strikes Zinaida on the cheek with his riding crop. I could hear the swish of the whip and feel the momentary keen and painful sting of its supple thong. This upset me in some unaccountable way, and at this point I had to stop reading and walk up and down the room. But Grandmother just sat there without moving a muscle, and even the hot, stifling air was quite motionless, as though it knew that I was busy and must not be disturbed. The room was getting hotter all the time. Mimi began to snore slightly. It was quiet—eerily quiet, with not a sound from the outside world. Everything seemed weird to me at that moment, and I wanted to run away from it all, but also to stay there forever. The darkening room, Grandmother's yellow eyes, her tiny figure wrapped in a shawl, hunched up and silent in the corner, the heat, the closed door, the crack of the whip, its loud swish—only now do I understand how bizarre all this was, and how much it affected me.

I was startled out of my troubled state by the ringing of the doorbell. It was Mr. Sorokin. I hated him at that moment. I hated his wretched scales, all this meaningless, futile, squawking music. It must be said that Sorokin was a splendid fellow. He had close-cut hair, fine large hands, and magnificent full lips. Today, under Grandmother's eye, he had to teach me for a whole hour—even a little over —and really give value for money. He got no credit for his pains. The old woman's eyes followed his every movement coldly and intently, and were quite indifferent and aloof to him. Grandmother had no time for strangers. She expected them to do their duty by us, and that was all.

We began our lesson. I was not afraid of Grandmother, but for a whole hour I had to bear the brunt of poor Sorokin's unusual devotion to duty. He felt very out of place in this remote room, in the presence of the peacefully sleeping dog and the frosty old woman sitting in the corner. At last he took his leave. Grandmother coldly gave him her large leathery and wrinkled hand, but she made not the slightest movement with it. As he left, he bumped into a chair.

I endured the following hour as well—Mr. L.'s Hebrew lesson—and the moment came when the door closed behind him, too. By now it was nightfall. Faraway specks of gold lit up in the sky. The deep shaft of our courtyard was flooded with moonlight. In the neighbors' apartment, a woman's voice began to sing, "Why do I love you so

madly?" The rest of my family had gone to the theater. I
felt depressed and tired. I had read so much and done such
a lot of work. The servant girl brought in the samovar.
Grandmother lit a lamp. This immediately mellowed the
room; the dark, massive furniture was bathed in soft light.
Mimi woke up, took a walk through the other rooms, and
then came back to us to wait for supper. Grandmother was
a great tea drinker. She had kept a gingerbread for me. We
both drank a lot of tea. The sweat began to glisten in the
deeply etched seams of her face. "Do you want to go to
bed?" she asked. "No," I replied. We began to talk, and
once again I listened to Grandmother's stories. Long, long
ago, there was a Jew who kept an inn. He was poor, married and weighed down by a large family, and he sold
vodka without a license. A government inspector came to
see him and started making trouble for him. He went to a
rabbi and said, "Rebbe, a government inspector is plaguing
the life out of me. Ask God to help me." "Go in peace," the
rabbi said to him. "The government inspector will quiet
down." The Jew went home. He found the inspector on the
doorstep of his inn. He was lying there dead, with his belly
all purple and swollen up.

Grandmother fell silent. The samovar hummed away.
The neighbor was still singing. Everything was covered
with blinding moonlight. Mimi began to wag her tail—
she was hungry.

"In the old days, people had faith," Grandmother said.
"Life was simpler. When I was a little girl, the Poles rebelled. We lived next to the estate of a Polish count. The
Czar himself used to come and visit him. They used to
make merry for seven days at a stretch. I would run up to
the hall after dark and look in through the lighted

windows. The count had a daughter, and she had the finest pearls in all the world. Then there was this rebellion. Some soldiers came and dragged the old count out onto the square. We all stood around and cried. The soldiers dug a hole in the ground. They wanted to blindfold the old man, but he said he didn't want it. He stood in front of them and gave them the order to shoot. He was a big man with gray hair. The peasants liked him. Just as they were burying him, a courier came racing up. He had a pardon from the Czar."

The samovar was slowly going out. Grandmother drank her last glass of tea, which had gone cold by now, and sucked a piece of sugar in her toothless mouth. "Your grandfather," she said, "was a great one for telling stories. He didn't believe in anything, but he trusted people. He gave away all his money to his friends, but when he came to them for help they threw him downstairs, and that made him a little queer in the head." And she went on to tell me about my grandfather. He was a big man with a sharp tongue, passionate and overbearing. He played the violin, wrote essays at night, and knew all languages. He was ruled by an insatiable thirst for knowledge and life. A general's daughter had fallen in love with their elder son, and this had been the son's undoing. He became a wanderer and a gambler, and he died in Canada at the age of thirty-seven. All Grandmother had left was my father and me. Everything else was gone. For her, day was turning into night and death was coming slowly. She fell silent again, then lowered her head and began to cry. "Study!" she suddenly said with great vehemence. "Study and you will have everything—wealth and fame! You must know *everything*. The whole world will fall at your feet and

grovel before you. Everybody must envy you. Do not
trust people. Do not have friends. Do not lend them
money. Do not give them your heart!"

She said no more. There was silence in the room. She
was thinking about years gone by and all her troubles. She
was thinking about my future, and her stern commandments pressed down heavily—and forever—on my weak,
untried shoulders. In the dark corner the iron stove glowed
red hot and gave off a fierce heat. I was hot and stifled,
and I wanted to run outside into the fresh air and escape,
but I hadn't even the strength to raise my head. There
was a crash of crockery in the kitchen. Grandmother went
in there. It was suppertime. The next moment, I heard
her harsh and angry voice. She was shouting at the servant
girl. I felt awkward and upset. She had just been full of
such peace and sadness. The servant was answering back.
"Get out, you little slut!" I heard my grandmother shout
with uncontrollable rage in an unbearably loud and shrill
voice. "I am the one who gives orders here! You are break-
ing my things. Get out!" I could not stand the raucous,
metallic sound of her voice. I could see her through the
half-open door. Her face was taut, her lower lip was
trembling with fury, her throat was all swollen. The
servant was trying to reply. "Get out!" Grandmother said.
Now everything was quiet. The servant, with hunched
shoulders and on tiptoe, as though she was afraid to hurt
the silence, crept out of the kitchen. We had supper without exchanging a single word. We ate well and plentifully,
and took our time over it. Grandmother's translucent eyes
were motionless, and I did not know what they were looking at.

LEAVES FROM MY NOTEBOOK

The Public Library
The Nine
Odessa
Inspiration

(1916-1917)

The sketches entitled "The Public Library," "The Nine," "Odessa," and "Inspiration" are probably the first work Babel published after "Mama, Rimma and Alla" and "Ilya Isaakovich and Margarita Prokofyevna," stories that were printed by Maxim Gorky in the November 1916 issue of his magazine The Chronicle (Letopis).* Under the heading Leaves from My Notebook (Moi listki), and signed quite transparently Bab-El, all four sketches appeared during the winter of 1916–1917 in the forgotten Petrograd daily, Journal of Journals (Zhurnal Zhurnalov). Never included in any collection of Babel's work, they shared the oblivion of Journal of Journals until a few years ago, when they were rediscovered by Soviet scholars.

A young writer's preoccupation with books, with potential subjects, with inspiration—in a word, with literature—is the theme of these sketches. They could be retitled "Where and how one reads," "How one tries to tell a story," "What one should write about," and "How one should not write." They tell us something of the path that Babel—aspiring writer as he then was—had been following for several years. Furthermore, they suggest that he was struggling to combine the particular qualities of the two masters whose influence he openly acknowledged, Gogol and Maupassant. To do so, Babel knew, would be to achieve a unique blend of Russian sensibility and French economy.

---

* These two stories were first published in English in *The Lonely Years, 1925–1939.*

"The Public Library" and "The Nine" can be considered exercises in the portrayal of character, attempts to sketch people with brevity, precision, and humor. The evident desire to make the prosaic come to life yields two portrait galleries in which the grotesque, the pathetic, and the comic are mingled.

In pointing out the dangers of undisciplined "inspiration," Babel sets an artistic standard that he was to follow in his lifelong struggle with the written word.

"Odessa" is a hymn to the city of Babel's youth and to the sun, the sun that had been so much ignored by Russian writers. He communicates his excitement over the cosmopolitan atmosphere of Odessa, over its lively, ludicrous, touching people, over a life that is so "extraordinarily interesting" that it calls for a poet of its own.

"Odessa" can also be read as an enthusiastic manifesto inspired by hope and ambition: hope that a Russian Maupassant would appear to dispel the northern fog and introduce lightness and ease to a literature of prevailing gloom; ambition to become himself that "literary Messiah" so long awaited, to return to the more Gallic prose tradition begun by Pushkin but eclipsed by naturalist realism, a mode, Babel felt, that had become barren. Transmuted into Socialist Realism, it was soon to be imposed on Russian literature, and Babel's celebrated silence of the thirties can be explained by reluctance to adopt the literary manner he challenged in this essay.

"The Public Library" (Publichnaya biblioteka) *and "The Nine"* (Devyat) *were first reprinted in the weekly* Literary Russia (Literaturnaya Rossia), *March 13, 1964. "Inspiration"* (Vdokhnovenie) *was first reprinted in the Moscow literary magazine* The Banner (Znamya), *No. 8, 1964, and was subsequently included in the volume* Collected Works (Izbrannoye) *with a preface by Ilya Ehrenburg, published in 1966. "Odessa"* (Odessa) *has not been republished in the Soviet Union, perhaps because of the views about literature expressed in it.*

The Public Library

You can feel straightaway that The Book reigns supreme here. All the people who work in the library have entered into communion with The Book, with life at second-hand, and have themselves become, as it were, a mere reflection of the living.

Even the attendants in the cloakroom are hushed and enigmatic, full of inward-looking calm, and their hair is neither dark nor fair, but something in between.

It is quite possible that at home they drink methylated spirits on Saturday nights and systematically beat their wives. But in the library they are as quiet as mice, self-effacing, withdrawn, and somber.

Then there is the cloakroom attendant who draws. His eyes are kind and woebegone. Once every two weeks, helping a fat man in a black jacket to take off his coat, he murmurs that "Nikolai Sergeyevich likes my drawings, and so does Konstantin Vasilyevich. I've only had elementary schooling, and where I go from here I really don't know."

The fat man listens. He is a reporter, a married man, fond of his food and overworked. Once every two weeks he goes to the library to rest—he reads about some trial or other, carefully copies out the plan of the building where the murder took place, is perfectly happy and forgets that he's married and overworked.

He listens to the attendant in anxious bewilderment and wonders how he should deal with someone like this. If he gives him a tip when he leaves, the man might be offended —he's an artist, after all. If he doesn't give him anything, he might still be offended—after all, he's an attendant.

In the reading room there are the more exalted members of the staff: the assistants. Some of them stand out by virtue of a pronounced physical defect—one has his fingers all curled up and another has a head which has dropped over on one side and got stuck there. They are dowdily dressed and extremely thin. They look as though they are possessed of some idea unknown to the world at large.

Gogol would have described them well!

Those assistants who don't "stand out" have gentle balding patches, neat gray suits, a prim look in their eyes, and a painful slowness of movement. They are always chewing something and moving their jaws, although they have nothing in their mouths, and they talk in a practiced whisper. Altogether, they have been debilitated by books, by not being able to have a good yawn every now and then.

Nowadays, during the war, the readers have changed. There are fewer students—scarcely any, indeed. Once in a blue moon you may see one pining away, without undue hardship, in a corner. He will be on a "white ticket," that is, will have a military exemption on grounds of health. He will wear horn-rimmed spectacles or cultivate a slight limp. There are also, however, those on state scholarships and hence temporarily exempted. They have a hangdog look, wear drooping mustaches, appear tired of life and very introspective: they keep reading a little, thinking a little, looking at the pattern of the reading lamp and burying themselves in a book again. They're supposed to graduate and go into the army, but they're in no hurry. Everything in its time.

Here's a former student who has come back in the shape of a wounded officer, with a black sling. His wound is healing. He is young and rosy-cheeked. He has had his dinner and taken a stroll down the Nevsky. The Nevsky is already lit up. The evening edition of the *Stock Exchange News* is already making its triumphal rounds. In Yeliseyev's[1] there are grapes cradled in millet seed. He's early for his evening engagement, so the officer, just for old times' sake, goes to the library. He stretches out his long legs under the table at which he is sitting and reads the *Apollon*. It's a little boring. Opposite sits a girl student. She is studying anatomy and copying a drawing of the stomach into her notebook. She looks as though she's from Kaluga or thereabouts—broad-faced, big-boned, rosy-cheeked, thoroughgoing, and tough. If she has a boyfriend, then that's the best thing for her: she's made for love.

Next to her is a picturesque tableau, an inevitable feature of any public library in the Russian Empire: a sleeping Jew. He is worn out. His hair is a burnished black. His cheeks are sunken. His forehead is bruised and his mouth is half open. He makes wheezing noises. Goodness knows where he comes from, or whether he has a residence permit. He reads every day, and he also sleeps every day. His face is a picture of overwhelming weariness and near-madness. He is a martyr to the book, peculiarly Jewish, an inextinguishable martyr.

Next to the assistants' counter there sits reading a large, broad-chested woman in a gray jumper. She is the sort who talks in the library in unexpectedly loud tones, frankly and ecstatically voicing her astonishment at the printed word and engaging her neighbors in conversation. Her reason for coming here is to find a way of making soap at home. She is about forty-five years old. Is she right in the head, they wonder.

Another regular reader is a lean little colonel in a loose-fitting tunic, wide breeches, and brightly polished boots. He has short legs and his mustaches are the color of cigar ash. He dresses them with brilliantine, as a result of which they run to all shades of dark gray. In days of yore he was so dumb he couldn't even make the rank of colonel and hence be retired as a major general. In retirement he has been an infernal nuisance to the gardener, the servants, and his grandson. At the age of seventy-three he took it into his head to write a history of his regiment. He writes surrounded by a mountain of materials. He is liked by the assistants, whom he greets with exquisite courtesy. He no longer gets on his family's nerves. The servant gladly polishes his boots.

There are all kinds of other people in the public library —too many to be described.

It is evening. The reading room is almost dark. The silent figures at the tables are a study in weariness, thirst for knowledge, ambition. . . .

Soft snow weaves its weft behind the large windows. Nearby, on the Nevsky, there is teeming life. Far away, in the Carpathians, blood is flowing. *C'est la vie.*

The Nine

THERE ARE NINE OF THEM. All of them want to see the editor. The first to come into his office is a burly young man with a loud voice and a bright tie. He introduces himself. His name is Sardarov and he writes satirical verses. He would like us to publish some of them. There is a foreword written by a famous poet. If need be, he can provide an epilogue as well.

The editor listens. He is a thoughtful, unhurried man who has seen many things in his life. He has all the time in the world: the magazine has gone to press. He looks through the verses:

"Oh," Franz Joseph moans in Vienna,

"Oh, I'm quite at the end of my tether . . ."

The editor says that unfortunately, etc. The magazine needs articles on the cooperative movement and features from abroad. . . .

Sardarov sticks out his chest, bows with excruciating good grace, and exits noisily.

Next comes a young lady—pale, shy, and very pretty. This is her third visit. Her poetry is not for publication. She just would like to know—and this is all she wants—whether it makes sense for her to go on writing it. The editor is very nice to her. He sometimes sees her on the Nevsky with a tall gentleman who every now and then very solemnly buys her half a dozen apples. This solemnity is dangerous, as her poems show only too well. They are the artless story of her life.

"*You want my body,*" she writes. "*Take it, my enemy, my friend, but where shall I find my heart's desire?*"

The editor thinks: "He'll take her body soon enough, the way things are going. How lost you look, with those helpless, pretty eyes. You won't find your heart's desire so quickly, but as a woman you will be quite piquant."

In her poems the girl describes her "*madly frightening*" or "*madly beautiful*" life and her various little troubles, as well as "*sounds, sounds, sounds around me, sounds that intoxicate, sounds without end . . .*" One can be sure that after the solemn gentleman has done his work, the girl will stop writing poetry and start visiting the midwife.

After the girl, the writer Lunev, a small and nervous man, comes in. His is a complicated story. Lunev once lost his temper with the editor. He is a bewildered person with a family, lots of talent, and no luck. In his agitation, in his frantic pursuit of money, he is not quite clear about whom he may shout at and whom he may not shout at. First he had sworn at the editor and then, before he knew what he was doing, he brought along his manuscripts, only to realize how stupid it was, how very hard life was, and what an unlucky devil he was. In the waiting room he had a slight attack of palpitation, and now in the editor's office he is told that his "little piece" is not bad, but that, *au fond*, it isn't literature, that it is really . . . Lunev feverishly agrees and starts muttering: "You are a good man, Alexander Stepanovich, and I was nasty to you . . . it can be understood in different ways . . . that's just what I wanted to bring out, but it's all much deeper, honestly it is . . ." Lunev flushes painfully. With trembling fingers he gathers together the sheets of his manuscript and tries to look either as though he couldn't care less or as though he regards the whole thing with irony—but God alone knows what he's trying to look like . . .

After Lunev come two types very familiar in editorial offices. The first is a pink, gushing, fair-haired lady. She gives off a warm whiff of scent. Her eyes are bright and childlike. She has a small son of nine, and this son: "Well, you know, he writes. He writes for days on end. At first we didn't take any notice, but all our friends are amazed, and even my husband—my husband works in the land-improvement department and he's a very down-to-earth person and has no time at all for modern literature, Andreyev, Nagrodskaya,[1] and all that—well even he had to laugh . . . I've brought you three of his exercise books . . ."

The other one is Bykhovsky. He's from Simferopol. He's a splendid fellow, brimming with life. He doesn't write, he has no particular business with the editor, and, in fact, he has nothing at all to say; but he is a subscriber and he has just dropped by to have a chat, to let us know his impressions, to get the feel of life in Petrograd. So get the feel of life in Petrograd he does. The editor mumbles something about politics, about the Cadets.[2] Bykhovsky beams and feels that he is taking an active part in the country's public life.

The saddest visitor is Korb. Korb is a Jew, a real Ahasuerus. He was born in Lithuania and got hurt in a pogrom in one of the southern towns. Since then he has bad headaches. Later he was in America. During the war he somehow turned up in Antwerp and at the age of forty-four he joined the French Foreign Legion. He got a concusssion at Maubeuge and his head shakes. Somehow or other he was evacuated back to Russia, to Petrograd. He gets some kind of pension, rents a corner of a stinking basement in Peski, and is writing a play called "The King of Israel." With his terrible headaches, he can't sleep at night, so he paces the basement and thinks. His landlord, a well-fed, supercilious man who smokes black, four-kopeck cigars, was angry at first, but then, disarmed by Korb's meekness and the industry that went into all those hundreds of pages of writing, he grew to like him. Korb wears an ancient, faded topcoat from his Antwerp days. His chin is covered with stubble, and in his eyes there is weariness, but also a fanatical look of determination. Korb has a headache, but he is writing a play and the first words of this play are: "Toll the bells, for Judaea has perished . . ."

After Korb there are just three more. One of them is a young man from the provinces—a slow, reflective type who takes a long time to sit down in the chair and is in no hurry to leave it. He slowly takes in the pictures on the walls, the clippings on the table, the portraits of staff members . . . What, actually, can we do for him? Actually, we can do nothing at all for him . . . He has worked on a newspaper . . . What sort of a newspaper? A provincial newspaper . . . And he was just wondering what our circulation was, and how much we paid . . . We explain to the young man that it is not always possible to answer such questions—

if he is a writer we could tell him, but if he isn't, then . . .
The young man replies that he isn't exactly a writer and
has no particular qualifications, but that he could be an
editor, for example.

The "editor" leaves and in comes Smursky. Smursky also
has quite a past. He used to be an agronomist in the Kashin
District of Tver Province. A quiet district and a wonderful
province, but Smursky was drawn to Petrograd. He had
offered his services as an agricultural expert and, what's
more, he had given twenty of his manuscripts to one of the
magazines. Two of them had been accepted. Smursky is
now convinced that his future is in literature. He no
longer offers his services as an agricultural expert. He
now goes around in a frock coat and carries a briefcase.
He writes every day and his output is considerable. He is
published rarely.

And the ninth visitor is none other than Stepan Drako,
"the only man to travel round the world on foot, King of
Life and public speaker."

Odessa

O DESSA IS AN AWFUL PLACE. Everybody knows how they murder the Russian language there. All the same, I think there's a lot to be said for this great city, which has more charm than any other in the Russian Empire. Just think how easy and straightforward life is in Odessa. Half the population consists of Jews, and Jews are people who are very clear about a few very simple things: they marry so they won't be lonely, they make love so their tribe will live forever, they make money so they can buy houses and give their wives astrakhan jackets, they're fond of children because—well, isn't it a very nice thing to love your children, and aren't you supposed to? Poor Jews in Odessa are very confused by provincial governors and official forms, but it's not easy to get them to abandon positions they took up a very long time ago. You can't get them to do that, but you can learn a lot from them. It's to a large extent because of them that Odessa has such an easygoing, straightforward atmosphere.

The Odessan is the opposite of a man from Petrograd. It's becoming axiomatic that Odessans do very well for themselves in Petrograd. They earn money there. Because Odessans are dark, the plump blondes of Petrograd fall in love with them, and, in general, they have a tendency to settle on the Kamennoostrovsky Prospekt. You might think

I'm just trying to be funny. No, sir. It's a matter of deeper things: the fact is that these dark Odessans bring a little sun and lightheartedness with them.

But apart from gentlemen who bring with them a little sun and a lot of sardines in the original cans, I think there must also come—and soon—the fructifying, life-giving influence of the Russian South, of Odessa, perhaps (*qui sait?*) the only city in Russia which might give birth to something we need so much: our own national Maupassant. I can even see some young girls, some very young girls (I'm thinking of Izya Kremer[1]), who augur well for the future of singing in Odessa: their voices are not very strong, but they have joy, artistically expressed joy in all their being, high spirits, lightness of touch, and a charming, sad, and touching feeling for a life which is both good and bad, but extraordinarily—*quand même et malgré tout*—interesting.

I have seen Utochkin,[2] an Odessan *pur sang:* nonchalant yet profound, reckless but thoughtful, handsome but too long in the arm, brilliant but stuttering. He is now a total wreck from cocaine or morphine—this, they say, happened after he fell out of an airplane somewhere in the marshes of Novgorod Province. Poor Utochkin—he has gone out of his mind, but I know for sure that there will soon come a time when Novgorod will make pilgrimages to Odessa.

Most of all, this city simply has the material conditions in which the talent of, say, a Maupassant could be nurtured. In its swimming pools in summer, the bronzed figures of muscular, young sports enthusiasts glisten in the sun, as do the powerful bodies of fishermen, who have no time for sport; then there are the fat, potbellied, and good-natured "commercial gentlemen"; the pimply,

scrawny dreamers, inventors, and brokers. And a little
way from the wide sea there are the smoking factories,
where Karl Marx is up to his usual business.

In Odessa there is a very poor, crowded, and much suffering Jewish ghetto, a very self-satisfied bourgeoisie, and
a very "Black Hundred"[3] city council.

In Odessa there are sweet and relaxing spring evenings,
the strong scent of acacias, and, over the dark sea, a moon
which radiates a steady, irresistible light.

In Odessa, in the evening, out at their comic and vulgar
dachas, fat and comic bourgeois lie in their white socks on
couches under a dark velvet sky, digesting their lavish
suppers, while in the bushes their powdered wives, fat
from idleness and naïvely corseted, are passionately
squeezed by ardent students of medicine and the law. In
Odessa the *luftmenschen* haunt the coffeehouses trying to
make a ruble to feed their families, but the pickings are
not good, and who would give a ruble to anyone as useless
as a *luftmensch?*

In Odessa there is a port, and in the port there are boats
hailing from Newcastle, Cardiff, Marseilles, and Port Said.
There are Negroes, Englishmen, Frenchmen, and Americans. Odessa has known prosperity, and now it's in decline
—a poetic, rather carefree, and very helpless decline.

"Odessa," the reader will say at last, "is a city like any
other city, and this is all special pleading."

All right, it's special pleading, and I suppose I'm really
doing it on purpose, but, *parole d'honneur,* there *is* something about the place. And this something will be seen
by anybody worth his salt, and he will say that, true
enough, life is sad and monotonous, but that all the same,

quand même et malgré tout, it is extraordinarily, but quite extraordinarily, interesting.

From these thoughts about Odessa my mind turns to deeper things. If one thinks about it, doesn't it seem that in Russian literature there has so far been no real, joyous, and vivid description of the sun?

Turgenev has given us the morning dew and the still of the night. In Dostoevsky you can feel under your feet the dismal, uneven roadway as Karamazov goes to the tavern, the heavy, mysterious fog of St. Petersburg. It is these dismal roads and shrouds of mist that stifle people and, in so doing, distort them in a way at once terrible and comic, giving rise to the noisome fumes of passions and making the usual human bustle even more frantic. Do you remember the bright, fructifying sun in Gogol, a man from the Ukraine? But such passages are rare. It is "The Nose," "The Overcoat," "The Portrait," and "Notes of a Madman" that predominate.

It is a victory of Petersburg over Poltava. Akaki Akakiyevich, modestly enough, but with terrifying preponderance, forces out Gritsko, and the work begun by Taras is finished off by Father Matvei.[4] The first Russian writer to speak about the sun with excitement and passion was Maxim Gorky. But the mere fact that it is done with excitement and passion means that it's still not quite the real thing.

Gorky is a precursor, and the most powerful one of our time. But he is not a poet of the sun, merely a herald of the truth that if there is any subject worthy of a poet, then it's the sun. In Gorky's love of the sun there's something cerebral, and it's only through his enormous talent that he can overcome this handicap. He loves the sun because Russia is rotten and devious, because in Nizhny, Pskov, and Kazan people are flabby, ponderous, unfathomable, pathetic, and sometimes immeasurably and stupefyingly boring. Gorky knows why he loves the sun, and why one should love it. It is this self-conscious approach that makes Gorky a precursor—often a magnificent one, but still only a precursor.

Now it may be that Maupassant doesn't know anything —or perhaps he knows everything there is to know. He has a carriage clattering down a road scorched by the heat, and in this carriage there's the fat, sly youth Polyte and a strapping, ungainly peasant girl. What they're doing in there, and why, is their own business. The sky is hot and the earth is hot. The sweat is pouring off Polyte and the girl, and the carriage is clattering down the road scorched by the heat. That's all there is to it.[5]

Recently there has been a spate of writing about how people live, love, kill, and conduct local elections in the province of Olonetsk, Vologda, or, for that matter, Archangels. All this is rendered in the authentic accents of the language exactly as it is spoken in Olonetsk or Vologda. We learn that life in these parts is bleak and primitive. We have heard all this before. And soon we shall be quite sick of reading about it. In fact, we're sick of it already. This is why I think Russians will be drawn to the South, to the sea and the sun. Though it's wrong to use the future tense here: they *have been* drawn there for many centuries. It is in her drive to the steppes, perhaps even in her drive to the "Cross of St. Sophia," that we may see Russia's essential path.

There is a feeling that the blood must be refreshed. The atmosphere is stifling. The literary Messiah who has been awaited so long and so hopelessly will come from there— from the sunny steppes washed by the sea.

Inspiration

I WANTED TO SLEEP, and I was in a bad mood. Just then Mishka came to read his story. "Shut the door," he said and pulled a bottle of wine out of his pocket.

"This is my day. I've finished my story. I think it's the real thing. Let's have a drink on it, friend."

Mishka's face was pale and sweaty.

"People who say there's no such thing as happiness are fools," he said. "Happiness is inspiration. I wrote all last night and didn't notice the dawn come. Then I walked around the town. The town is extraordinary, early in the morning: dew, silence, and very few people. Everything is crystal-clear and you can see the day coming: cold and blue, ghostly and gentle. Let's drink, friend. I'm as sure as sure can be: this story's a turning point in my life." Mishka poured himself some wine and drank. His fingers quivered. He had a hand of remarkable beauty—slender, white, and smooth, with tapering fingers.

"You know, I must place this story," he went on. "They'll take it anywhere. They print such rubbish nowadays. The main thing is to have some pull. I've had a promise. Sukhotin will fix everything . . ."

"Mishka," I said, "you should go through it again—nothing's crossed out . . ."

"To hell with it—plenty of time for that . . . At home,

you know, they just make fun of me. *Rira bien qui rira le dernier.* I don't say a thing, you know. In a year's time we shall see what we shall see. They'll come crawling . . ."

The bottle was nearly empty.

"Stop drinking, Mishka . . ."

"I have to pep myself up," he replied. "Last night I smoked forty cigarettes." He took out an exercise book. It was very thick, very thick indeed. I played with the idea of asking him to leave it with me. But then I looked at his pale forehead, on which a vein had swollen up, at his wretched, twisted necktie, and I said: "Very well, Leo Tolstoy . . . when you write your autobiography, remember me . . ."

Mishka smiled. "Bastard," he replied. "You don't value my friendship at all."

I settled myself comfortably. Mishka bent over his exercise book. The room was quiet and half in darkness.

"In this story," Mishka said, "I have tried to do something new, something shrouded in a haze of wonder, full of tenderness, half shades, and allusiveness . . . I am utterly sick of the crassness of our life . . ."

"Cut out the preliminaries," I said. "Start reading . . ."

He began. I listened attentively. It was not easy: the story was bad and boring. A salesclerk had fallen in love with a ballerina and spent all his time hanging about under her window. She went away and the salesclerk was upset because his dream of love had been disappointed.

Soon I stopped listening. The words in the story were boring, hackneyed, and smooth, like polished wooden counters. Nothing came through: what sort of a fellow the salesclerk was, what she was like.

I looked at Mishka. His eyes were on fire. He ground
his cigarettes, as they went out, between his fingers. His
dull face which had been grievously narrowed and need-
lessly foreshortened in the making, his large, protruding,
yellow nose, his swollen, pale-pink lips—they all grew
brighter and slowly, with steadily mounting force, filled
with the joyfully self-confident flush of creativity.

He read with agonizing slowness and when he had
finished, he clumsily pocketed the exercise book and looked
at me. . . .

"You see, Mishka," I said slowly, "you see, this needs
some thought . . . The idea is very original, and the tenderness comes through . . . but you see, the way you've
written it . . . It'll have to be polished a little, you
know . . ."

"I've been working on this thing for three years," Mishka
replied. "There are some rough bits, of course, but taken
as a whole . . ."

Something had gotten home to him. His lip trembled.
He hunched his shoulders and took an awful long time to
light a cigarette.

"Mishka," I said, "it's a wonderful thing you've written.
You're still a little short on technique, but *ça viendra*. My
God, what a lot you've got in that head of yours . . ."

Mishka turned around and looked at me. His eyes were
like a child's: loving, bright and happy.

"Let's go out," he said. "It's stuffy in here."

The streets were dark and silent.

Mishka pressed my hand hard and said: "I'm as sure as
sure can be: I have talent. My father wants me to find a

job. I'm not saying a thing. In autumn it's Petrograd for me. Sukhotin will fix everything."

He paused, lit a new cigarette from the previous one, and went on more quietly: "Sometimes I feel such inspiration it hurts. Then I know that what I'm doing is right. I sleep badly—nightmares all the time and feeling really miserable. I turn over and over for three hours in bed before I get to sleep. In the morning my head aches with a terrible, dull kind of pain. I can only write at night, when there's nobody around and it's quiet, and I'm all on fire. Dostoevsky always wrote at night and drank tea by the samovar while he was at it, but I have my cigarettes . . . You should just see the smoke in my room . . ."

We reached Mishka's home. His face was caught in the light of a street lamp. An eager, thin, sallow, and happy face it was.

"We'll show 'em, God damn it!" he said and squeezed my hand even more tightly. "In Petrograd everybody makes it."

"All the same, Mishka," I said, "one has to work . . ."

"Sashka, my friend," he replied with a broad and condescending smile, "I'm no fool—I know what's what. Don't worry, I'm not resting on my laurels. Come by tomorrow, we'll take another look."

"All right," I said, "I'll come."

We said good night. I went back home. It was all very depressing.

Shabos Nahamu

(1918)

"Shabos Nahamu" was originally published in the Social Democrat newspaper Evening Star *(Vechernyaya zvezda)* on *March 16, 1918. It has, in the last few years, undergone full "rehabilitation." Its first reappearance was in the literary magazine* The Banner, *No. 8, in 1964, and it was included in both Soviet editions of Babel's* Collected Works *published in 1966.*

Written with apparent gusto, "Shabos Nahamu" is based on a traditional Jewish tale. It is a kind of farce, earthy and gently sarcastic. Though we have no comparable stories from Babel's pen, he certainly planned to write more about the hero of this one, since it is subtitled "From the cycle Hershele." *Hershele Ostropoler, a character in the folklore of the Pale of Settlement, is the Jewish manifestation of a universal archetype, the trickster, somewhat similar to Tyll Eulenspiegel.*

Jews were to remain prominent in Babel's future work, but they were never again portrayed so lightheartedly. He was to witness too many acts of violence against them, perhaps, to continue making simple fun of stereotypes. Between 1918 and 1923, Hershele, the folk character, was ousted by Benya Krik, the Jewish gangster.

Shabos nahamu *is Hebrew for "Sabbath of Comfort." The fast day of Tisha B'au, which commemorates the destruction of the First and Second Jewish Temples—by the Babylonians in*

586 B.C. and by the Romans in A.D. 70—is followed by a Sabbath of relief from mourning. *This Sabbath,* shabos nahamu, *derives its name from Isaiah 40, which is read in the synagogue on that day and which begins* Nahamu, nahamu, *"Comfort ye, comfort ye."*

Shabos Nahamu

THE MORNING GOES BY, the evening comes—and it's the
fifth day of the week. Another morning goes by, the
evening comes—and it's the sixth day. On the sixth day, on
Friday, you have to pray. When you've prayed, you take
a stroll through the *shtetl* in your best hat and then come
back home for supper. When he gets home, a good Jew
has a glass of vodka—neither God nor the Talmud says he
can't have two—and eats his gefilte fish and his currant
cake. After supper he feels good. He tells stories to his wife;
then he goes to sleep with one eye closed and his mouth
open. He sleeps, but his wife in the kitchen hears music, as
though the blind fiddler had come from the *shtetl* and was
standing under the window playing.

That's how it is with every Jew. But Hershele was different from other Jews. No wonder he was famous in all
of Ostropole, in all of Berdichev, and in all of Vilyuisk.
Hershele celebrated only one Friday in six. On the others
he sat with his family in the darkness and cold. His children cried, and his wife gave him hell. Each reproach was
as heavy as a cobblestone. Hershele used to answer back
in verse.

Once, so the story goes, Hershele thought he would look
ahead a little. He went off to the fair on Wednesday to earn
some money for Friday. Where there's a fair you'll find a

pan, and where there's a *pan* you'll find ten Jews. But you'd
be lucky to earn three pennies from ten Jews. They all
listened to Hershele's funny stories, but when it was time
to pay, they weren't around any more. Hershele went back
home with a belly as empty as a wind instrument.

"What did you earn?" his wife asked.

"I earned life everlasting," he said. "Both the rich and
the poor promised it to me."

Hershele's wife had only ten fingers. She bent them
back one by one. Her voice was like thunder in the mountains. "Every other wife has a husband like everybody
else's. But I have a husband who feeds his wife on funny
stories. May God take away the use of his tongue, and his
hands, and his feet in the New Year."

"Amen," Hershele said.

"In everybody else's windows the candles burn as if
they'd set fire to oak trees in the house, but I have candles
as thin as matches, and there's so much smoke from them
it shoots up to heaven. Everybody else has white bread,
but all my husband brings me is firewood as wet as newly
washed hair—"

Hershele said not a single word in reply. Why add fuel
to the flames when they're burning so brightly as it is?
That's point number one. And then, point number two,
what can you say to a cantankerous wife when she's right?
When she got tired of shouting, Hershele went and lay
down on his bed and thought, "Maybe I should go and see
Rabbi Boruhl?" (Everybody knew that Rabbi Boruhl suffered from black melancholia and that only Hershele with
his talk could make him feel better.) "Maybe I should go
to Rabbi Boruhl? It's true the *tsadik's* servants give me
only bones and keep the meat for themselves. Meat is bet-

ter than bones, but bones are better than air. I'll go to
Rabbi Boruhl."

Hershele got up and went out to harness his mare. She
gave him a stern and sad look.

"It's all very well, Hershele," her eyes said, "you didn't
give me any oats yesterday, you didn't give me any oats the
day before yesterday, and I didn't get anything today
either. If you don't give me any oats tomorrow, I'll have to
start thinking about whether I'm going to live."

Hershele flinched before her searching look, lowered
his eyes, and stroked her soft lips. Then he sighed so loud
that the mare understood everything, and he said: "I'll go
to Rabbi Boruhl on foot."

When Hershele set off, the sun was high in the sky. The
sweltering road ran on ahead. Carts drawn by white oxen
and piled with sweet-smelling hay lumbered slowly along.
Peasants sat on these high carts, dangling their legs and
swishing their long whips. The sky was dark blue, and the
whips were black. When he'd gone about five miles,
Hershele reached a forest. The sun was already leaving its
place in the sky, which was ablaze with gentle fires. Barefoot girls were bringing the cows in from the fields. The
cows' pink udders, heavy with milk, swayed to and fro.

The forest met Hershele with cool shade and soft twilight. Green leaves bent over and stroked each other with
their flat hands, whispered together faintly up there in the
treetops, and then fell back, rustling and quivering, into
their places. Hershele did not hear their whispering. The
orchestra playing in his belly was as big as anything hired
by Count Potocki for a gala evening. He still had a long
way to go. Dusk was hurrying in from the edges of the
earth, closing in over Hershele's head, and spreading out

across the world. Unblinking lamps lit in the sky, and the earth fell silent.

It was night when Hershele arrived at an inn. A light was burning in a small window. Zelda, the landlady, was sitting in her warm room by this window, sewing baby clothes. Her belly was so big it looked as if she were going to have triplets. Hershele looked at her small red face with its light-blue eyes and wished her good evening. "Can I stop here and rest for a while, ma'am?"

"Sure you can."

Hershele sat down. His nostrils heaved like a pair of blacksmith's bellows. There was a red-hot fire blazing in the stove. Water was boiling in a large caldron and frothing over snow-white dumplings. A fat chicken was bobbing up and down in a golden broth. There was a smell of currant cake from the oven. Hershele sat on a bench writhing like a woman in labor. More plans were hatching in his head at that moment than King Solomon ever had wives. It was quiet in the room, the water was boiling, and the chicken tossed and pitched on its golden waves.

"Where is your husband, ma'am?" Hershele asked.

"My husband has gone to the *pan* to pay his rent," she said, and paused. Her childlike eyes grew round and large. Suddenly she went on: "And I am sitting here at the window thinking. I would like to ask you a question. I suppose you travel up and down the world, and you've studied with the rabbi, and you know about our Jewish ways. But nobody ever taught me anything. Tell me: will *shabos nahamu* be coming soon?"

"Oho," thought Hershele, "a very good question indeed. All kinds of potatoes grow in God's garden."

"I'm asking because my husband promised me that when

shabos nahamu comes, we'll go and visit my mother. And I'll buy you a dress, he says, and a new wig, and we'll go to Rabbi Motalemi to ask him for a son to be born to us instead of a daughter. But that will only be when *shabos nahamu* comes. I suppose he's a man from the other world, this *shabos nahamu?*"

"You are quite right, ma'am," Hershele replied. "God himself put those words into your mouth. You will have both a son and a daughter. I am *shabos nahamu*, ma'am."

The baby clothes slipped from Zelda's knees. She got up and bumped her head on a rafter, because she was tall, Zelda was, and plump and red and young. Her high breasts looked like two bags tightly packed with grain. Her light-blue eyes opened wide like a child's.

"I am *shabos nahamu*," Hershele repeated. "For two months now I've been doing my rounds, helping people. It's a long journey from heaven down to earth. My shoes are all worn out. I bring you greetings from all your people up there."

"From Aunt Pesya?" Zelda shouted, "and from Father, and from Aunt Golda? You know them?"

"Who doesn't know them?" Hershele said. "I often talk with them just like I'm talking with you now."

"How are they getting on up there?" Zelda asked, clasping her trembling hands on her belly.

"Not too well," Hershele replied sadly. "What sort of life do you think it is for a dead person? There isn't much fun up there."

Zelda's eyes filled with tears.

"They're cold," Hershele went on, "and hungry. They eat the same as angels, you see. They're not supposed to eat more than the angels. And how much do angels eat?

They're quite happy with a drink of water. You wouldn't get a glass of vodka up there once in a hundred years."

"Poor Father," Zelda whispered, quite shaken.

"At Passover you get a *latke*, and one blintze has to last you twenty-four hours."

"Poor Aunt Pesya," Zelda shuddered.

"I have to go hungry myself," Hershele continued, and turned his face away as a tear rolled down his nose and fell into his beard. "There's nothing I can do about it, you see: up there I'm treated like everybody else—"

Hershele didn't manage to get any further. With a patter of her large feet, Zelda bore down on him with plates, bowls, glasses, and bottles. When Hershele began to eat, she saw that he really was a man from the other world.

To start off with, Hershele had chicken liver garnished with fat and chopped onion. He drank it down with a glass of high-class vodka flavored with orange peel. Then he had fish, mashing soft boiled potatoes into the savory sauce that went with it and putting half a jarful of red horseradish on the side of his plate—a horseradish at the mere sight of which five *pans* in all their finery would have wept tears of envy.

After the fish Hershele did his duty by the chicken and the broth with blobs of fat swimming in it. The dumplings, bathed in molten butter, jumped into Hershele's mouth like hares fleeing from a hunter. We don't have to say anything about what happened to the currant cake. What do you think happened to it, if you consider that Hershele sometimes never saw a currant cake from one end of the year to the other?

When he had finished, Zelda got together all the things

that she had decided to ask Hershele to take to the other world for Father, Aunt Pesya, and Aunt Golda. For her father she put out a new prayer shawl, a bottle of cherry brandy, a jar of raspberry jam, and a pouch full of tobacco. For Aunt Pesya she got out some warm gray socks, and for Aunt Golda an old wig, a large comb, and a prayer book. Lastly, she gave Hershele a pair of boots, some goose cracklings, and a silver coin.

"Give them our regards, Mister Shabos Nahamu, give them all our kind regards" were her parting words to Hershele as he set off with the heavy bundle. "Or would you like to wait a little until my husband comes back?"

"No," said Hershele. "I must be on my way. You don't think you're the only one I have to look after, do you?"

When he had gone about a mile, Hershele stopped to draw breath, threw the bundle down, sat on it, and took stock of the situation. "As you well know, Hershele," he said to himself, "the world is full of fools. The landlady in that inn was a fool. But perhaps her husband is not a fool, perhaps he has large fists, fat cheeks, and a long whip. If he comes home and chases after you in the forest, what then?"

Hershele wasted no time seeking an answer to this question. He immediately buried the bundle in the ground and marked the spot so that he would be able to find it again.

Then he ran back the way he had come, stripped naked, put his arms around a tree, and began to wait. He did not have to wait long. At dawn Hershele heard the crack of a whip, the smacking lips of a horse and the thud of its hooves. This was the innkeeper in hot pursuit of Mister Shabos Nahamu.

When he reached the naked Hershele with his arms around a tree, the innkeeper stopped his horse and looked as silly as a monk on meeting the devil.

"What are you doing here?" he asked.

"I am a man from the other world," Hershele replied gloomily. "I have been robbed of important papers which I was taking to Rabbi Boruhl."

"I know who robbed you," shouted the innkeeper. "I have a bone to pick with him too. Which way did he go?"

"I cannot tell you which way he went," Hershele whispered bitterly. "If you will lend me your horse I will soon catch up with him, while you wait for me here. Undress and stand by this tree. Hold it up and do not leave it until I return. It is a holy tree, and many things in our world depend on it."

Hershele only had to take one look at a man to see what he was made of. He had seen right away that the innkeeper was not much brighter than his wife. And sure enough, the innkeeper got undressed and stood by the tree. Hershele climbed onto the cart and drove back to where he had left the bundle. He dug it up and went on to the edge of the forest.

Here Hershele shouldered the bundle again, left the horse, and took the road which led to the house of the holy Rabbi Boruhl. It was morning already. The roosters were crowing with their eyes shut. The innkeeper's horse wearily plodded back with the empty cart to the place where she had left her master.

He was waiting for her, huddled against the tree, naked under the rays of the rising sun. He was cold, and he kept shifting from foot to foot.

DIARY

Mosaic
A Fine Institution
The Blind Men
Evacuees
Premature Babies
The Palace of Motherhood

(1918)

The six journalistic pieces entitled "Mosaic" (Mozaika), "A Fine Institution" (Zavedenitse), "The Blind Men" (Slepye), "Evacuees" (Evakuirovanniye), "Premature Babies" (Nedonoski), and "The Palace of Motherhood" (Dvorets materinstva) were published in Gorky's Petrograd journal New Life (Novaya zhizn) in the spring of 1918. This is their first republication in any language.

In the pages of New Life, Gorky openly showed his distrust of the Bolshevik party and of Lenin's methods. He warned against the dangers of a premature seizure of power, and after the Kerensky government had been overthrown, he attacked the triumphant Bolsheviks with vehemence. The following excerpt from an editorial published on November 7, 1917, is representative:

Lenin, Trotsky, and their supporters, have already been poisoned by the corruptive virus of power, which is evident from their disgraceful treatment of freedom of speech and person, and of all those rights for which democracy has struggled . . . The workmen must understand that, with their skins and blood, Lenin is performing an experiment . . . that there are no miracles in ordinary life, that they must expect hunger, complete dislocation of industry, ruin of transport, prolonged bloody anarchy—and in its wake no less bloody and gloomy reaction. That is where the people are being led by its present leader. We must recognize that Lenin is not an omnipotent magician, but a cold-blooded trickster, who spares neither the honour nor the lives of the proletariat.*

The opinions expressed in New Life *inevitably invited reprisals. Before long, articles were heavily censored and occasionally an entire issue was banned.* New Life *was completely suppressed by Lenin toward the end of 1918, leaving Gorky without an independent publication. But the following year, when the Civil War threatened the very life of the Revolution, Gorky made his peace with the Bolsheviks and rallied to the side of Lenin.*

It is likely, judging by Babel's six pieces for New Life, *that in 1918 he not only followed Gorky's literary advice but shared his mentor's outlook on the political situation. Indeed, these pieces illustrate by example the criticisms of the new regime made in Gorky's editorials.*

Both men were basically in sympathy with a revolution that claimed to give power to the dispossessed, but they were also most sensitive to any abuse of power. Recently back from fighting on the Rumanian front, Babel must have realized that his ambition to become an Odessan "poet of the sun" would have to be postponed in favor of more urgent tasks. Thus, for a time, he became a chronicler of the chaos which had engulfed Petrograd and of which, by force of circumstances, he was a witness.

Visiting Petrograd's new social institutions as a reporter, Babel saw an almost total failure of efforts to improve the people's lot, and waste, disorder, and corruption as well. He

* M. Gorky, *Revolyutsia i kultura, Statyi za 1917* (Berlin, 1920), p. 55. (Not republished in the Soviet edition of Gorky's collected works.) I am indebted for this quotation to the stimulating and useful work of Richard Hare, *Maxim Gorky, Romantic Realist and Conservative Revolutionary* (London: Oxford University Press, 1962), pp. 94–95.

was profoundly affected by what he was describing, whether it was a socialist maternity ward or a home for juvenile delinquents, and his tone ranges from biting irony to exasperated indignation. The six pieces read like a denunciation of a regime both muddled and shortsighted, of a social order which could lavish attention on its corpses (as in "Evacuees") yet fail to succor the living.

The spectacle of this neglected and abused humanity, the result of the "heedless destructiveness" of these years, filled Babel with fear for the future of his country.

Even today, this whole period in the careers of Gorky and Babel is an embarrassment for Soviet critics. For instance, a recent commentator observes:

As we know, Gorky made serious political mistakes during this period and he was far from a proper understanding of the October Revolution. This came out very clearly in the articles he published in *New Life,* for which Babel also worked. His sketches, signed "Bab-El," were mainly about everyday life and they gave an extremely one-sided impression of revolutionary Petrograd. Privation, neglect, havoc, cases of barbarism and injustice are the main topics of these cursory impressions which usually appeared under the general heading "Diary." True, the author of this diary noted signs of things to come, constructive measures taken by the young Soviet regime, and cases of genuine socialist concern for the workers. But even here Babel sometimes demonstrated that unstable, diffuse, and passive humanism which he himself was to condemn a few years later in *Red Cavalry.**

* I. A. Smirin, "Noviye materialy—Na puti k konarmii," in *Literaturnoye nasledstvo,* Vol. 74, 1965, pp. 472–473.

Mosaic

IT WAS SUNDAY—a day of rest and springtime—and Comrade Shpitsberg was giving a lecture in the halls of the Winter Palace. He had entitled it: "The all-forgiving personality of Christ and the vomit of Christianity."

Comrade Shpitsberg calls God "Mr. God" and priests he refers to as "potbellied sky pilots." He describes all religions as the "shopwindows of charlatans and exploiters," denounces the Popes of Rome, bishops, archbishops, Jewish rabbis, and even the Tibetan Dalai Lama, "whose excrement is considered by the besotted Tibetan masses to have healing properties."

In a corner of one of the halls an attendant is sitting. He is cleanshaven, thin, and has an air of calm. There is a knot of people around him—old women, workers who look pleased with life, soldiers with time on their hands. The attendant is telling them about Kerensky, about the bombs that went off under the floors, about the ministers pressed up against the smooth walls of the dark, echoing corridors, about the feathers scattered from the pillows of Alexander III and Maria Fyodorovna.[1]

His tale was interrupted by an old woman who asked: "Where is the lecture here, mister?"

"Antichrist is in the Nicholas Hall," the attendant replied impassively.

A soldier standing nearby laughed. "Antichrist in the Nicholas Hall, and you stand here talking your head off like this?"

"I'm not frightened of him," the attendant said, just as stolidly as before. "I live with him day and night."

"You must have a fine old time, then . . ."

"No," said the attendant, looking at the soldier with faded eyes. "I do not have a fine old time. I have a dreary time with him."

And the old man mournfully told the smiling people around him that this devil of his was small and timid, went around in galoshes, and seduced schoolgirls on the sly. The old man wasn't allowed to finish. He was led away by other attendants, who explained that after October he had gone "slightly off his head."

I walked away in some amazement. Here was this old man who had seen the Czar, the uprising, bloodshed, death, and feathers from the Czar's pillows. And now, if you please, Antichrist had descended on him. And Satan could find nothing better to do than to dream of schoolgirls, trying not to get caught as he prowled in the Admiralty district.

What dreary devils we have.

Shpitsberg's sermon about the end of "Mr. God" is obviously a flop. His audience is listless and the applause is thin. It was very different a week ago, after a similar exhibition of "plain, anti-God talk." On that occasion four people distinguished themselves: a church warden, a frail

little deacon, a retired colonel in a fez, and a burly shopkeeper from the Gostiny Dvor.[2] They advanced onto the
platform and after them came a crowd of women and
ominously silent shop assistants.

The deacon began in unctuous tones: "We must pray,
my friends," and he ended in a whisper: "Not all are
asleep, my friends. At the tomb of Father Ioann[3] we recently made a solemn vow. Organize, my friends, in your
parishes."

When he left the platform he added, his eyes half closed
in rage and his thin body trembling: "How cunning they
are, my friends. About the rabbis, about the rabbis, mark
you, they never say a word . . ."

Then the church warden thundered: "They have destroyed the spirit of the Russian army." "We won't let
them!" shouted the colonel in the fez. "The swindlers!"
screeched the shopkeeper in a deafening, brutish voice.
The disheveled, bareheaded women crowded around the
smirking churchmen, the lecturer was driven from the
rostrum, and two Red Guard workers, who had been
wounded at Pskov, were forced up against the wall. One
of them shook his fist and shouted: "We know what you're
up to! In Kolpino[4] they say Mass till two in the morning.
The priest has thought up a newfangled service and turns
it into a political meeting . . . We'll make those church
domes shake . . ."

"No, you won't, you devil," a woman said in a hollow
voice, stepping back and crossing herself.

During Easter service in the Kazan cathedral the con-
gregation is standing with lighted candles. The small, yel-

low flames flicker with their breathing. The cathedral is packed from end to end. The service goes on for an unusually long time. The priests walk about in gleaming mitres. Behind the Crucifix electric lights have been skillfully installed. Christ seems to be stretched out in the dark blue of a starry sky.

In his sermon the priest says the Holy Countenance is once more averted in unbearable pain, everything sacred is being spat on and reviled by the ignorant, "who know not what they do." The tone of the sermon is sorrowful, obscure, portentous. "Come to the Church, to our last bulwark, for it will not forsake you."

A little old woman is praying by the door of the cathedral. She says to me lovingly: "The choir's singing so nicely, they do have fine services nowadays . . . Last Sunday the Metropolitan himself was here . . . There was never anything as grand as this before . . . Even the workers from our factory go to church . . . People are tired, they've had too much worry, but it's nice and quiet in church, and there's the singing. A real rest, it is."

A Fine Institution

During the "Social Revolution" nobody has had finer intentions than the People's Commissariat of Welfare. Its schemes are audacious indeed. It has been entrusted with tasks of the highest importance: to produce an immediate explosion in the soul of man, to usher in by decree a reign of universal love, and to prepare citizens for a life of dignity in free communes. The Commissariat has gone about these aims in no uncertain manner.

Under the Welfare Commissariat, there are institutions clumsily described as "homes for juveniles convicted of socially dangerous acts." These homes were supposed to be set up along completely new lines, in accordance with the latest findings of the psychologists and the educators. The Commissariat's plan was indeed put into effect along very new lines.

Among the people appointed to run one of these new homes was a doctor from Murman[1] whom nobody had heard of before. Another appointee—also from Murman—had been a minor railroad clerk. This latter social reformer is now standing trial for cohabiting with some of his female charges and for freely spending the free commune's funds. His pleas to the court—he was the director of the home—are semi-literate, querulous, and overpoweringly redolent of a prerevolutionary police station. He describes himself as "devoted body and soul to the holy cause of the people" and says he has been betrayed by "counterrevolutionaries." In applying for the post in the Welfare Commissariat, this worthy citizen made reference to his "political outlook as a party worker and a Bolshevik." This, it seems, was all that was needed to qualify as an educator of juvenile delinquents.

The other people in charge of the home are: a Latvian woman who speaks poor Russian and had four grades of schooling the Lord only knows where; a former dancer who went to a "natural school" and had been in ballet for thirty years; a former Red Army man who previously worked as sales assistant in a tea store; a semi-literate clerk from Murman; a girl clerk, also from Murman. In addition, five "governors" (there's a good Communist word for you!) were assigned to the boys.

How they all spent their time was described to officials as follows: "After a day on duty, they sleep a day, then rest a day; they do as they please; if they want the floors washed, they just make someone do it." It should be noted that one of the homes, for forty children, had a staff of twenty-three.

How these people, many of whom are now up for trial, managed their affairs was disclosed by an inspection of the accounts. Hardly any statements of expenditure were signed and it was impossible to make out how the money had been spent. Receipts didn't show to whom payment was made, and—in the case of salaries—for what period. The traveling expenses of one minor staff member came to 455 rubles for January of this year.

If you go to the home, you will find that there is no teaching and sixty percent of the children can barely read or write. The food consists of soup made of roots, and salt herring. There is a terrible stench from broken sewage pipes. No attempt has been made to disinfect the premises, despite the fact that there have been ten cases of typhus. Sickness is rampant. On one occasion a boy with frostbitten toes was brought in late at night. He had to lie in a corridor till morning because nobody could be bothered with him. Escapes are frequent. At night the children are sent naked to the damp lavatories—their clothes are hidden to keep them from running away.

To sum up: The homes maintained by the Welfare Commissariat are stinking holes that bear a remarkable resemblance to pre-reform[2] prisons. The administrative and teaching personnel consists of people left over from the old regime who have fastened on to the "people's cause," but have no connection with welfare and, in most cases, no qualifications. Why they were accepted for employment by the workers' and peasants' government is anybody's guess.

All this I have seen myself: the sullen, barefoot children, the puffed, pimply faces of their gloomy mentors, and the broken sewage pipes. Our poverty and wretchedness are truly unsurpassed.

The Blind Men

THE NOTICE OUTSIDE READ: "Home for Blind Veterans."
I rang the bell at the high oak door. Nothing happened. The door, it turned out, was open. I went in and this is what I saw.

A tall, black-haired man in dark glasses is coming down a broad staircase. He is feeling his way with a cane. Now he has successfully negotiated the stairs and could go in any one of a number of directions—there are passageways, vestibules, steps, and rooms off to the side. The blind man's cane taps softly on the smooth, gleaming walls. He holds his head stiffly, keeping it well back. He moves slowly, gropes for a step with his foot, trips, and falls. A trickle of blood breaks the surface of his white, domed forehead, flows down his temple and behind the lens of his round spectacles. The dark man raises himself, feels the blood with his fingers, and calls softly: "Kablukov." The door of a room nearby opens noiselessly. There is a flurry of walking sticks as other blind men come to help their comrade. Some of them can't find him, press close to the walls, and turn unseeing eyes upward; others take him by the arm, lift him from the floor, and with bowed heads wait for a nurse or an orderly.

A nurse comes in. She takes the men back to their various rooms and explains: "This sort of thing happens every day. The building is just not suitable. What we need is something simple and easy to walk around in, with good corridors. This place is a death trap with all these steps . . . Every day somebody falls . . ."

As we all know, our authorities display particular zeal when it is a question of leaving in a hurry. Whenever people are being evacuated or things are being moved hither and thither with ruinous consequences, the activities of the powers-that-be take on a hectic air of gay inventiveness and voluptuous intensity.

I was told how the blind men had been evacuated from their home. The initiative for the move had come from the men themselves. The approach of the Germans and fear of occupation[1] had caused great agitation among them. The reasons for this agitation were complex. First, any kind of crisis is relished by the blind—they are quickly and easily seized by excitement and the nervous pursuit of an imaginary goal banishes for a moment the gloom of their darkness. The second reason for getting out was their particular fear of the Germans. Most of them had been prisoners of war and were convinced that if the Germans came they would again have to work for them and starve. "You are blind," the nurses told them. "Nobody needs you and they won't do anything to you." To which they replied: "The Germans won't let anybody off, they'll find work for us all. We've lived among them, nurse . . ."

This anxiety was touching—and typical of former prisoners of war. The blind men asked to be moved deep inside

Russia. Since it was a matter of evacuation, permission was granted in no time at all. Then their troubles began.

With determined looks on their thin faces, the blind men trudged in heavy clothes to the station. Their escorts later told the story of their wanderings. The day they left, it was raining, and the disconsolate veterans, huddled in the open, had to wait all night before they were put on a train. They traveled the country in cold, dismal freight cars, going from one local Soviet to another, standing in line for rations in filthy waiting rooms. Bewildered, silent, and straight as ramrods, they meekly followed their tired and angry escorts. A few of them headed for the country-side. But the countryside did not want them. Nobody wanted them. They were useless, human flotsam; and, like blind puppies, they journeyed from station to station, look-ing for a home. But there was no home for them, and they returned to Petrograd. In Petrograd all was quiet—very quiet, indeed.

Tucked away not far from the main building was a one-story house given over to an unusual sort of people created by these unusual times: blind men with families.

I got talking with one of the wives, a dumpy woman in a smock and Caucasian slippers. Her husband was a gaunt old Pole whose face had turned orange from the gas that had eaten into his skin. After a couple of questions I realized that the small, bewildered woman was a Russian, typical of those who had been caught up in the whirl-wind of war with all its calamities and dislocation. At the beginning of the war she had become a nurse, "out of patriotism." She had been through and seen a great deal:

badly wounded soldiers, German air raids, dances in officers' clubs, officers in cavalry breeches, illness, a fleeting love affair, then—revolution, propaganda, another love affair, evacuation, and committee work . . .

Once upon a time, in Simbirsk or somewhere, she had had parents, a sister Varya, and a cousin who worked on the railroad . . . But she hadn't had a letter from her parents in a year and a half, her sister Varya was far away, the warm smell of home had grown faint . . . Now, instead, there was weariness; she had grown fat, she had nothing to do but sit by the window, her lackluster eyes wandering slowly from one object to another; and then there was this husband, the blind Pole with the orange face . . .

There are several women like this in the home. They don't leave because they have no reason to and nowhere to go. The nurse in charge often says to them: "I just don't know what this place is supposed to be . . . We're all crowded in here together, but you shouldn't be here . . . I don't even know what to call the place any more. We're down as an official institution, but it's hard to tell at present . . ."

In a dark room with a low ceiling, two pale, bearded peasants are sitting opposite each other on narrow beds. Their glass eyes never move. In soft voices they talk about the land, about wheat, about the price of pigs nowadays . . .

In another room a frail and bored old man is teaching a tall, strong soldier to play the violin. Weak, squeaky sounds flow quaveringly from beneath the bow . . .

I move on. From one of the rooms I hear a woman's groans. I look in and see a girl of about seventeen doubled up in pain on a broad bed. Her tiny face is purple. Her swarthy husband is sitting in a corner on a low stool, weaving a basket with sweeping movements of his hands and listening intently but coldly to her groans.

She married him six months ago. Soon, in this unusual house occupied by unusual people, a child will be born. It will indeed be a child of our times.

Evacuees

ONCE UPON A TIME there were factories, and factories were the seat of injustice. Nevertheless, in those unjust days the chimneys sent up smoke, the flywheels spun silently, the steel shone brightly, and the factory buildings quivered with the vibrant hum of work.

Then justice was done. But it was done badly. There was no more steel. People were paid off. Listless and baffled, they were hauled in trains from place to place.

Obedient to an iron law, working people are now aimlessly wandering the earth, like specks of dust valued by nobody.

A few days ago they started "evacuating" the Baltic Works.[1] They shoved four workers' families into a railroad coach, loaded the coach on a ferry, and sent it on its way. I do not know whether the coach was properly secured on the ferry or not. Some say it was scarcely secured at all.

Yesterday I saw these four "evacuated" families. They were lying side by side in the morgue. Twenty-five corpses —fifteen of them children. All the names were just right for this kind of dreary disaster: Kuzmin, Kulikov, Ivanov. None of them was older than forty-five. All day long, women from Vasilyev Island and the Vyborg Side[2] crowded between the white coffins. Their faces were just as gray as those of the drowned.

They wept sparingly. Anyone who has been to a cemetery knows that people no longer shed tears at funerals. They are harassed and have no time, their minds are constantly prey to petty, nagging thoughts.

The women were sorry most of all for the children, and they placed ten-kopeck notes on their small, folded hands. The bosom of one of the dead women, with a five-month-old baby still clutched to her, was covered with money.

I came out. Two bent old women were sitting on a rotting bench by a gate in a cul-de-sac. They were gazing with bleary, watery eyes at a brawny janitor lighting a fire to melt the black, soft snow. Dark rivulets began to trickle over the muddy earth. The old women were whispering together about all the little details of their daily lives. The carpenter's son had joined the Red Guards and got killed. There were no potatoes in the markets, nor would there be. A Georgian had come to live in the building and was doing business in candies. He had got a general's daughter—she was still just a schoolgirl—to live with him; he drank vodka with the militia and the money was rolling in.

Then one of the old women began to tell, in her rough and simple way, why twenty-five people had fallen into the Neva.

"The engineers have all left the factories. The Germans[3] say the land belongs to them. The people hung around for a while, then they left their quarters and started leaving for home. So the Kulikovs, you see, set off for Kaluga. They made a raft. Three days it took them. Some of them were drinking and some of them were so fed up they just sat around thinking. There were no engineers, and these people don't know a thing. They finished the raft and off it floated and they were waving goodbye. Then the water got rough and they all fell in, women and little children and all . . . But they fixed them up nicely . . . eight thousand rubles they gave for the burial . . . what a nice service they're getting, and their coffins all done up in brocade . . . really doing the working people proud, they are . . ."

Premature Babies

THE WARM WHITE WALLS are suffused with even light. You cannot see the Fontanka spreading like a shallow puddle down below. Nor can you see the heavy lacework of the embankment,[1] on which swollen piles of ordure are stranded in a black mush of crumbling snow.

Women glide noiselessly in gray or dark dresses through the warm, high-ceilinged rooms. Along the walls, deep down in small metal cots, their stern eyes open wide, lie silent midgets—the puny offspring of wasted, under-sized women with hard hearts, women from the murky, wooden slums of the city's outskirts.

When they are brought in, the premature babies weigh about a pound, or a pound and a half. Over each cot is a graph—the baby's crooked lifeline. Only now it's not so crooked. The line is straightening out. Life burns in the pound-weight bodies with a sad and ghostly flame.

Still another little-noticed aspect of our decline is that women who breast-feed have less and less milk.

There are not many wet-nurses here. Just five for thirty babies. Each of them feeds one of her own and four others; that's just how they say it in the patter of the place: "One of her own and four others." They have to suckle the babies every three hours. They get no time off. They can sleep only two hours at a time, never more.

Every day these women, whose breasts are sucked seven times every twenty-four hours by five small blue mouths, are given three eighths of a pound of bread.

They stand around me, all five of them, big-breasted but thin, in their nunlike clothing, and say: "The lady doctor tells us we're not giving enough milk and the babies aren't putting on any weight . . . There's nothing we'd like better . . . It's as if they were sucking our blood . . . If they'd only treat us the same as cab drivers . . . They told us in the ration office: 'You're not workers . . .' Two of us went out to try to buy something just now, but our legs gave way under us. We stopped and looked at each other, we thought we'd fall down, we just couldn't go on."

They ask me to do something about ration cards and extra allowances. Standing along the wall, they bow their heads; their faces are red, flustered, pitiful, like the faces of women begging favors in government offices.

I start to leave. The matron comes after me and whispers: "They're all very high-strung . . . You can't say a word without their crying . . . We just keep quiet and cover up for them. A soldier comes to see one of them here, well, so what—let him . . ."

I hear the story of the woman who is visited by a soldier. She came to the home a year ago—a short, tiny person who knew her business. The only thing not small about her were her heavy, milk-laden breasts. She had more milk than any of the other wet-nurses. Since then a year has gone by, a year of ration cards, of a diet of *koryushka*,[2] and of a great increase of tiny wizened bodies hastily extruded by the faceless, hardhearted women of Petrograd. Now this small, businesslike woman has no milk. She cries if her feelings are hurt and when she is feeding she sullenly thrusts out her empty breasts and turns her face away. Why can't they give this small woman an extra three eighths of a pound of bread, put her on the same footing as a cab driver, or do something . . . They ought to have more sense—it's for the children's sake. If they don't die, they will grow up to be boys and girls, and they will have to make some sort of life for themselves. And suppose they go and make just three eighths of a life for themselves? A stunted kind of life that will be. We've seen enough of that kind of life, the stunted kind.

The Palace of Motherhood

T HEY SAY it was built by Rastrelli.[1]
It has a wine-red façade whose sameness is relieved
by slender columns—those certain hallmarks, trim and
brooding, of imperial Petropolis—and it is less grand than
the Yusupov and Stroganov palaces,[2] which are so magnificent in the subtlety and simplicity of their perfection.

It originally belonged to Razumovsky[3] and later became
a school for orphaned girls from good families. The orphaned girls from good families had a headmistress, and
the headmistress lived in twenty-two light-blue, high-
ceilinged rooms.

Both Razumovsky and the headmistress have gone.
Eight big-bellied women shuffle in slippers, with the heavy
footfall of pregnancy, along Rastrelli's corridors. There
are only eight of them, but the palace is all theirs. And it's
now called The Palace of Motherhood.

Eight women of Petrograd with gray faces and legs
swollen from too much running around. All they have
known are months of waiting in line in cooperative stores,
factory whistles calling their husbands to the defense of
the Revolution, the grim anxiety of wartime, and now the
throes of a Revolution which is carrying them off into the
unknown.

Our heedless destructiveness is now blandly presenting
its bills in the shape of famine and unemployment. There's
nothing to do for the men coming back from the front,
their wives have no money on which to bear children, the
factories hold up their cold chimney stacks to the heavens.
The haze of paper—with money and all kinds of other
things printed on it—which has floated like a mirage
before our stupefied faces is beginning to fade away. But
the earth turns as before. People die and people are born.

I am glad to be able to talk about the tiny, life-giving
flame that has been kindled in these bare rooms. It is good
that the premises have not been allotted to committees
concerned with confiscation and requisition. It is good
that the white tables are not awash with thin cabbage
soup and that here there is none of the all too familiar talk
about arrests.

This house will be called The Palace of Motherhood.
The decree announcing it says that it is to "help women
in their great and difficult task." It is a break with the
prison atmosphere of the old homes for waifs and strays,
where the children died or, if they were lucky, grew up
as "wards." Children must live. They must be born for the
sake of a better way of life.

At least, that's the idea. It has to be done properly.
Some time or other we must have a revolution.

Maybe it's sometimes not a bad idea to pick up guns
and start shooting at each other. But that's not all there
is to revolution. For all we know, it may have nothing
whatsoever to do with revolution.

We must see to it that children are born properly. This
is real revolution—of this I am quite sure.

The Palace of Motherhood opened three days ago. The district soviets have sent the first patients. A beginning has been made. Now we shall see. It is proposed to start a school of motherhood. Anybody who wants will be able to come. They will be taught hygiene and child care. This is something that has to be learned. At the beginning of the century, as many as forty percent of the women in our maternity homes died in childbirth. The figure was never lower than fifteen to twenty percent. Now, with undernourishment and anemia, the death rate has risen even higher. Women will be admitted to the palace in their eighth month of pregnancy. For six weeks before they give birth they will live in restful surroundings, eating properly and doing work of the right kind. They won't have to pay anything. The bearing of children is to the benefit of the state, and the state must pay for it. After giving birth they will stay in the palace for ten, twenty, or forty days—until they are fully recovered. They used to leave the maternity home on the third day ("There's no one to look after the house, and the children have to be fed"). It is proposed to start a school for "stand-in housekeepers" who will look after the women's homes while they are in the palace.

There are already the beginnings of a museum and permanent exhibition. Here mothers will be able to see a good, simple cot, baby clothes and baby food. They will also see what syphilis and smallpox sores look like; they will read our statistical diagrams giving infant-mortality figures—we're tired of hearing them, but they are the first of their kind in the world. They will be able to buy, for very little, baby clothes, diapers, and medicines.

This is the first flush of the idea—the *revolutionary* idea —of the "socialization of women."

The first eight women—wives of sailors and workers— have come to these spacious halls which belong to them. They must be kept for them and thrown wide open to them all.

OBSERVATIONS ON WAR

On the Field of Honor
The Deserter
Old Marescot's Family
The Quaker

(1920)

In 1920 the short-lived "literary, critical, and political journal"
Lava *started publication in Odessa. Two issues came out—in*
June and July—before it folded. The first included four stories
by Babel: "On the Field of Honor" (Na pole chesti), *"The*
Deserter" (Desertir), *"Old Marescot's Family"* (Semeistvo
papashi Marescot), *and "The Quaker"* (Kvaker).

"On the Field of Honor," alone among these stories, has been
reprinted in Russian—in the New York literary magazine Aerial
Ways (Vozdushniye puti), *No. 3, 1963.*

"What I have told here is true," writes Babel at the end of
"On the Field of Honor." "It is described in Captain Gaston
Vidal's book Figures et anecdotes de la Grande Guerre. *He*
witnessed it." And indeed this is so. "Vidal (le capitaine Gas-
ton) né à Saint-Etienne (Loire) en 1888" published in 1918
his "authentic" account of some of the actions he had partici-
pated in or witnessed during the First World War. ⃰ *Babel*
must have read Vidal's book after returning from service on
the Rumanian front and not long before joining Budyonny's
First Cavalry in the summer of 1920. The fact that he chose to
read this book—a rather chilling documentary though of
doubtful literary value—and then to "translate" parts, indicates

⃰ Gaston Vidal, *Figures et anecdotes de la Grande Guerre* (Paris: La
Renaissance du Livre, 1918).

*how preoccupied he was with the subject of war and the need
to find a new literary treatment for it.*

*Captain Vidal's original is a garrulous, romantic portrayal of
violence and cruelty. The writing is padded with clichés and
jingoistic and rhetorical flourishes punctuated by exclamation
marks. He is eloquent about "German aggression" and "the
old Gallic blood" that runs in the veins of French soldiers. But
the conflict Vidal describes remains one-dimensional despite
all the heroics.*

Babel's three adaptations of this original are an exercise in
compression and precision. Entire passages are replaced by a
single sentence. Factual elements are kept, but the melodra-
matic verbiage is stripped away, leaving only their essential
brutality. Emotionalism gives way to dry matter-of-factness
and Babel often strikes a humorous note lacking in the French
text.*

*For instance, the two opening sentences of "The Deserter"
read: "Captain Gémier was a splendid fellow, and something
of a philosopher as well. On the field of battle he would stop
at nothing, but in private life he didn't take offense at small
things." This is based on Vidal's original: "In battle he is a*

---

* The last of the *Lava* stories, "The Quaker," is the only one which is
not based on Captain Vidal's book. It has been impossible to locate a
literary source for this story, and perhaps none exists. The complex and
conflicting feelings of its two protagonists, as well as the Quaker's chief
characteristics—he is a man of peace among soldiers, an intellectual
unable to kill, a lover of horses—seem to foreshadow the narrator of the
Red Cavalry stories.

"On the Field of Honor" and "The Deserter" are based on two
incidents described by Vidal in Chapter XI (*Deux actes devant une
conscience*) of his book.

Chapter XV (*Histoire Shakespearienne*) is the source of "Old Marescot's Family." Babel considerably reduced the Shakespearean flights
of Vidal's version and, as usual, replaced his grandiloquence with a
tone of brisk irony. On the other hand, the interview with Monsieur
Marescot, particularly the final part with all its eeriness, is an almost
exact translation of the French.

raging lion; at rest, a brooding eagle. In battle, he throws him-self into this terrible, bloody adventure heart and soul, for his country, solely for his country, the one object of his thoughts. He has that fiber all great captains have. He knows neither fear for himself nor pity for the enemy nor indulgence for his own men when they commit an error. His mind is made of marble; he locks up his heart and commands with a rectitude which tolerates neither retreat nor weakness. In civilian life, you will find him a kind and peaceful man, a perfect husband and a perfect father, as we say, friendly and helpful, overlook-ing the slight wrongs that might be done to him. He knows how to forgive, how to make himself loved, and also how to philosophize." *

Babel described his method in an introductory note for the four Lava stories: "The stories published here are the begin-ning of my observations on war. The subject matter is bor-rowed from books written by French soldiers and officers who saw action. In some passages the plot and narrative technique are changed. In others I have tried to stick close to the orig-inal." By changing the intonation, turning descriptive passages into dialogue, making the original dialogue much terser, Babel drove home the point. Vidal's accounts lose their old-fash-ioned, vainglorious ring and become far more disquieting.

The Lava stories were the last Babel published before he joined Budyonny's First Cavalry for its Polish campaign. On

---

* C'est à la guerre un lion qui rugit, au repos un aigle qui médite. A la guerre, tout à l'aventure terrible et sanglante, il se donne corps et âme à son pays, rien qu'à son pays, seul objet de ses pensées. Il a l'âme qu'il faut aux chefs. Il ne connait ni la peur pour lui, ni la pitié pour l'ennemi, ni l'indulgence pour ses propres hommes quand ceux-ci commettent des erreurs ou des fautes. Il se fait un cerveau de marbre, se verrouille le coeur, commande avec une fermeté qui n'admet ni le recul ni la faiblesse. Au repos, il redevient le doux homme du temps de paix, bon père et bon époux, comme on dit, affable et serviable, oublieux des petits torts qu'on peut avoir envers lui, sachant pardonner, sachant se faire aimer, sachant aussi philosopher.

*his return he began work on the Red Cavalry stories and by
then he had seen enough not to need Captain Vidal's recollections any more. He had also found his own unmistakable
literary identity.*

On the Field of Honor

G ERMAN BATTERIES were bombarding the villages with heavy artillery. The peasants were fleeing toward Paris. With them they trailed cripples, misshapen children, sheep, dogs, and household utensils. The sparkling sky, dark blue and torrid, slowly became livid and swollen as it hazed over with smoke.

The sector near N. was held by the 37th Infantry Regiment. Its losses were enormous. It was preparing to counterattack. Captain Ratine was inspecting the trenches. The sun was at its height. From the neighboring sector it was learned that all the officers in number 4 company had been killed. The company was still holding out.

Three hundred meters from the trench, Ratine saw a human shape. It was the enlisted man, Bidoux, the poor imbecile Bidoux.[1] He was sitting squirming at the bottom of a dank hole in the ground. It had been made by a shell. He was doing what is done, to give themselves pleasure, by lewd old men in the villages and by dirty little boys in public lavatories. The less said about it, the better.[2]

"Close up your fly, Bidoux," the captain said with disgust. "What are you doing here?"

"I . . . I don't know what it is . . . I'm afraid, Captain . . ."

"Some wife you've found yourself here, you filthy swine! You have the nerve to tell me to my face that you're a coward, Bidoux. You have left your comrades at this moment, when the regiment is about to attack. . . . *Ben, mon cochon! . . .*"

"I swear it, Captain . . . I've tried everything. . . . 'Bidoux,' I said to myself, 'come to your senses.' . . . I've drunk a bottle of spirits to get my courage up. *Je peux pas, capitaine.* . . . I'm afraid, Captain! . . ."

The poor imbecile put his head on his knees, covered it with his two arms, and began to cry. Then he peered up at the captain with a glimmering of timid, submissive hope in the slits of his porcine eyes.

Ratine was a hot-tempered man. He had lost two brothers in the war and a wound on his neck had not yet healed. The soldier was engulfed by blasphemous abuse, he was assailed by a dry broadside of those sickening, furious, and senseless words which make the blood throb in the temples and after which one man kills another.

Instead of replying, Bidoux slowly shook his round head with its tousled red hair, the hard head of a village idiot.

No power on earth would make him stand up. Then the captain stepped up to the edge of the hole and hissed very quietly: "Get up, Bidoux, or I'll wet you from head to foot."

He did as he had said. A foul-smelling jet hit the soldier full in the face. Bidoux was an imbecile and a village idiot, but he couldn't take this insult. He gave a long-drawn-out, inhuman cry; this desolate, forlorn wail of despair was carried over the churned-up fields; the soldier started up, put out his hands, and ran across the field toward the

German trenches. An enemy bullet went right through his chest. Ratine finished him off with two shots from his revolver. The soldier's body never so much as twitched. It remained where it was between the lines.

Thus died Célestin Bidoux, a Norman peasant from Aury,[3] at the age of twenty-one, on the blood-stained fields of France. . . .[4]

What I have told here is true. It is described in Captain Gaston Vidal's book *Figures et anecdotes de la Grande Guerre*. He witnessed it. He also fought for France, Captain Vidal.

The Deserter

CAPTAIN GÉMIER was a splendid fellow, and something of a philosopher as well. On the field of battle he would stop at nothing, but in private life he didn't take offense at small things. That's something, if a man doesn't take offense at small things. He loved France with a heart-consuming love, and his hatred for the barbarians defiling its ancient soil was, therefore, unextinguishable, merciless, and as lasting as life itself.

What else can one say about Gémier? He loved his wife, he had brought up his children to be good citizens, he was a Frenchman, a patriot, a Parisian, a lover of books and of beautiful things. And now, on one bright, rosy morning in spring, it was reported to Captain Gémier that an un-armed soldier had been picked up between the French and enemy lines. His intention to desert was plain, his guilt beyond doubt, and he was brought in under guard.

"It's you, is it, Bauji?"

"It's me, Captain," the soldier replied, saluting.

"You thought you would take advantage of the dawn to go out for a breath of fresh air?"

The soldier said nothing.

"*C'est bien,* you may leave us." The guards went out

and Gémier locked the door after them. The soldier was twenty years old.

"You know what's coming to you, don't you? *Voyons,* tell me all about it."

Bauji hid nothing. He said that he was tired of the war: "I'm very tired of the war, *mon capitaine!* Six nights running now I haven't been able to sleep for the shells. . . ." The war was hateful to him. He hadn't been going to commit treason but to surrender.

Altogether, he was unexpectedly eloquent, this little fellow, Bauji. He said he was only twenty. *Mon Dieu, c'est naturel,* anyone could make a mistake at that age. He had a mother, a girlfriend, *de bons amis.* He had his whole life ahead of him, this twenty-year-old Bauji, and he would make up for the wrong he had done his country.

"Captain, what will my mother say when she hears I've been shot like the worst sort of criminal?" The soldier fell on his knees.

"You won't get my sympathy like that, Bauji!" the captain said. "You were seen by other soldiers. Five men like you, and a whole company gets infected. *C'est la défaite. Cela jamais.*[1] You're going to die, Bauji. But I'm giving you a way out just before you do. They won't learn about your disgrace in the *mairie.* Your mother will be told that you died an honorable death in battle. Let's go."

The soldier went out after his commanding officer. When they came to the wood, the captain stopped, took out his revolver, and handed it to Bauji.

"Here's how you can avoid a court-martial. Shoot yourself, Bauji. I'll come back in five minutes. Everything must be over by then."

Gémier walked away. Not a single sound disturbed the silence of the wood. The captain went back. Bauji, his shoulders hunched, was waiting for him.

"I can't, Captain," he whispered. "I don't have the strength. . . ." And he started off again about his mother, his girl, his friends, and about having his whole life ahead of him. . . .

"I'll give you another five minutes, Bauji! Don't make me waste my time just walking around for nothing."

When he returned, the soldier was lying sobbing on the ground. His fingers were clutching the revolver and moving slightly.

Gémier then pulled him to his feet and, looking him in the eye, said in a gentle, kindly tone of voice, "Bauji, my friend, perhaps you don't know how to do it?"

Without hurrying, he took the revolver out of the youth's wet hands, walked back three paces, and shot him through the head.

Gaston Vidal writes about this incident in his book. The soldier actually was called Bauji.[2] Whether the name Gémier I have given the captain is the right one, I can't really say. Vidal's story is dedicated to a certain Firmin Gémier "in token of deep respect." I think this dedication gives the game away. Of course the captain was called Gémier. And then, Vidal tells us that the captain really was a patriot, a soldier, a good father, and not a man to take offense at small things. That's something, if a man doesn't take offense at small things.

Old Marescot's Family

WE ENTERED A VILLAGE which we'd won back from the enemy. It was a small Picardy hamlet, charming and unpretentious. Our company was given the graveyard. All around were broken crucifixes, fragments of tombstones and slabs shattered by the hammer of an unknown despoiler. Moldering corpses spilled out of their coffins smashed by shells. A picture worthy of you, Michelangelo!

A soldier has no time for mysticism. A field of skulls has been churned up into trenches. That's war. We were still alive. If we were fated to swell the population of this cool corner, at least we would have made these moldering old geezers dance a little to the rousing tune of our machine guns.

A shell had lifted up the slab of one of the vaults. This had been done by way of offering me a resting place—no doubt about it. I took up my quarters in this hole: *que voulez vous, on loge où on peut.*

So here we were on a bright clear spring morning. I was lying on corpses, looking at the lush grass and thinking of Hamlet. He wasn't a bad philosopher, the poor prince. He had skulls talking back to him in human language. A knack like that would come in handy for a lieutenant of the French army nowadays.

The corporal called me: "Lieutenant, there's a civilian here wants to see you."

What the devil did a civilian want in this world of the dead? A character appeared on the stage: a faded, down-at-the-heels creature. He was gotten up in his best frock coat. The frock coat was spattered with mud. From his cowed shoulders there dangled a half-empty sack. There must have been frozen potatoes in it: every time the old man made a movement, something inside it creaked.

"*Eh bien,* what do you want?"

"I am Monsieur Marescot, you see," the civilian said in a whisper and bowed. "That's why I've come . . ."

"I don't follow . . ."

"I should like to bury Madame Marescot and the rest of the family, *monsieur le lieutenant!* . . ."

"What did you say?"

"My name, you see, is père Marescot." The old man lifted his hat above his ashen forehead. "Perhaps you've heard of me, *monsieur le lieutenant. . . .*"

Père Marescot? I had heard this name. Of course I had heard it. Here is the story: three days before, at the beginning of our occupation, all civilians had been ordered to evacuate the village. Some had left and others had stayed; those who had stayed had taken to the cellars. Their courage was of no avail under bombardment, stone walls proved a poor defense, and some were killed. One entire family had been buried under the ruins of their basement, and this was the Marescot family. Their name —such a good French name—had stuck in my memory. There had been four of them—father, mother, and two daughters. Only the father had come out alive.

"My poor fellow, so you are Marescot? It's all very sad. What on earth were you doing in that wretched cellar?"

I was interrupted by the corporal: "Looks as though they're starting up, Lieutenant . . ."

This was to be expected. The Germans had noticed signs of life in our trenches. The barrage started on the right flank and then shifted to the left a little. I grabbed père Marescot and pulled him down. My men, as good as gold, got their heads down and sat dead-still under cover; none of them showed so much as the tip of his nose.

"Frock-coat" went pale and looked uncomfortable. A little kitten of a six-incher went miaow not far away from us.

"What do you want? Tell me and look sharp about it! You can see that things are pretty hot around here."

"*Mon lieutenant,* I've told you everything: I'd like to bury my family."

"Very well, I'll have someone get the bodies."

"I have the bodies here, lieutenant!"

"What do you say?"

He pointed at the sack. It did indeed contain the meager remains of père Marescot's family.

I shuddered with horror.

"All right then, I'll give the order for them to be buried."

He looked at me as though I had uttered a total absurdity.

"When this damned noise dies down," I went on, "we'll dig a splendid grave for them. It will all be attended to, père Marescot, you need not worry . . ."

"But . . . but I have a family vault . . ."

"Very well then, show me where it is."

"But . . . but . . ."

"What do you mean, 'but'?"

"But, lieutenant, we're right in it here."

The Quaker

I T SAYS IN THE COMMANDMENTS: "Thou shalt not kill."
That's why Stone, a Quaker, had enlisted as a driver.
He was serving his country without committing the terrible sin of murder. With his education and means, he
could have got a more exalted position, but, a slave of his
conscience, he meekly accepted menial work and the company of people whom he found uncouth.

What was Stone? A bald dome on top of a pole. The
Lord had given him a body only to lift up his thoughts
above the petty cares of this world. His every movement
was no less than a victory of mind over matter. At the
wheel of his car, however calamitous the situation, he
bore himself with the wooden stiffness of a preacher in the
pulpit. Nobody ever saw him laugh.

One morning, when he was not on duty, he took it into
his head to go for a walk in order that he might pay
homage to his Maker in the midst of His creation. With a
huge Bible under his arm, he strode with his long legs
across meadows brought back to life by the spring. The
sight of the clear sky, the chirping of sparrows in the grass
—all this filled him with joy.

Stone sat down and opened his Bible, but at that moment he saw at the turning of a lane an untethered horse

with emaciated flanks through which the ribs showed. Immediately he felt a powerful call of duty: at home he was a member of the society for the protection of animals. He went up to the animal, stroked its soft lips, and, forgetting about his walk, set off back to the stables. On the way, his Bible with its clasps still firmly held in his hands, he let the horse drink at a well.

The stableboy was a youth by the name of Baker. The ways of this young man had long been a cause of righteous indignation to Stone: at every stopping place Baker left behind an unconsolable sweetheart.

"I could report you to the major," said Stone, "but I trust that, for this once, what I am about to say to you will suffice. This poor, sick horse, which I have brought here and which you are going to look after, is deserving of a better fate than you."

And he stalked off with measured, solemn steps, ignoring the loud guffaw behind him. The stableboy's square, jutting chin was convincing testimony to a stubbornness that would never be overcome.

A few days went by, but the horse still wandered around untended. This time Stone spoke to Baker in no uncertain terms, addressing him roughly as follows: "It may be, spawn of Satan, that the Almighty has granted you the right to destroy your own soul, but your sins should not be allowed to fall with all their weight on an innocent horse. Just look at it, you scoundrel. It is walking around here in a state of great distress. I am sure that you are ill-treating it, as one might expect from a blackguard like you. Let me repeat, sinner: go to your doom as fast as you will, but attend to this horse, or you will have me to reckon with."

From this day onward Stone felt that providence had entrusted him with a special mission: to care for this mal-treated quadruped. He thought that people, for their sins, were scarcely worth bothering about, but he felt boundless compassion for animals. His grueling duties did not prevent him from keeping his promise to God. He often got out of his car at night—he slept in it all curled up on the seat—to go and make sure that the horse was well out of range of Baker's studded boot. If the weather was fine he would mount his beloved animal, and the poor thing, prancing with an air of importance, would bear his long lean body at a trot across the fields now turning green. His face sallow and drained of blood, his pale lips closed tight, Stone recalled the deathless, mirth-provoking figure of the Knight of the Mournful Countenance trotting on his Rosinante amid flowers and tilled fields.

Stone's persistence bore fruit. Feeling himself under constant observation, the groom went to great lengths not to be caught in the act. But whenever he was alone with the horse, he visited on it all the savagery of his vile nature. For some reason he couldn't explain, he was frightened of the silent Quaker and because of this fear he hated Stone and despised himself. The only way in which he could raise himself in his own eyes was by tormenting the horse which Stone had befriended. Such is the contemptible pride of humans. Locking himself in the stable with the horse, the groom pierced its hairy, hanging lips with red-hot needles, beat it on the back with a lash made of wire, and threw salt in its eyes. When, left alone at last, the tortured animal, blinded by stinging salt and lurching like a drunken man, fearfully went to its stall, the groom lay down on his belly and laughed for all he was worth, enjoying his revenge.

After a change in the position at the front, the division to which Stone belonged was transferred to a more dangerous place. His religious beliefs did not allow him to kill, but they permitted him to get killed himself. The Germans were advancing toward the Isère. Stone was transporting the wounded. Round about him people of various nationalities were dying fast. Old generals, their faces clean and knobby, stood on hilltops and spied out the land through field glasses. The big guns roared incessantly. The earth gave off a stench and the sun poked around in the mangled corpses.

Stone forgot about his horse, but after a week his conscience started to nag him again. Seizing the first opportunity, the Quaker went back to the place where they had been before. He found the horse in a dark shed that had been knocked together from rotting planks. The animal was so weak it could hardly stand, and its eyes were covered with a dull film. It whinnied faintly at the sight of its faithful friend and laid its head, which it could scarcely hold up, on his hands.

"It's not my fault," the groom said insolently. "They're not giving us any oats."

"Very well," Stone replied, "I'll get some."

He looked at the sky shining through a hole in the roof, and went out.

I met him a few hours later and asked him whether the road wasn't dangerous. He seemed more self-absorbed than usual. The last few bloody days had left a deep mark on him and he looked as though he was in mourning for himself.

"No trouble so far," he said in a hollow voice, "but there may be at the end of it." And he added, for no apparent reason: "I've come foraging. I have to find some oats."

The next morning he was found dead at the wheel of his car by some soldiers who had been sent to look for him. A bullet had gone right through his skull and his car was in a ditch.

This was how the Quaker Stone died on account of his love for a horse.

An Evening at the Empress's

(1922)

"An Evening at the Empress's" (Vecher u imperatritsy) *was originally published in 1922 in the first issue of the Odessa magazine* Silhouettes *(Siluety), with the subtitle "From a Petersburg Diary." It was reprinted for the first time in 1964 in the Moscow magazine* The Banner, *No. 8, and was included in the Soviet* Collected Works *with a preface by Ilya Ehrenburg, published in 1966.*

The narrator of the story recalls an evening spent alone in the library of the Dowager Empress shortly after the Revolution. Babel reworked the same material as part of the horrifying and more complex "The Journey" (Doroga), published in 1932 (with the vague date 1920–1930) in the literary magazine 30 Days *(30 dnei). Though different details are stressed in the later story, the idea remains the same: the evocation of a past forever gone against the background of Revolutionary realities.*

An Evening at the Empress's

I HAD some red caviar and a pound of bread in my pocket. But nowhere to go. I was standing on the Anichkov Bridge, huddled up against Clodt's horses. A swollen night was closing in from the Morskaya. Orange lights, wrapped in absorbent cotton, were weaving down the Nevsky. I needed a place to shelter. Hunger was plucking at me like a clumsy kid playing a fiddle. I went over in my mind all the apartments abandoned by the bourgeoisie. The great squat hulk of the Anichkov Palace heaved into my line of vision. That was the place for me.

I had no trouble slipping unobserved through the entrance hall. The palace was empty. The faint scratching of an unhurried mouse could be heard in one of the side rooms. Here I was in the library of the Dowager Empress Maria Fyodorovna.[1] An old German was standing in the middle of the room, putting absorbent cotton in his ears. He was about to go to bed. My luck was really kissing me on the lips: I knew this German. I had once typed out for him, free of charge, a declaration about his lost identity papers. He belonged to me with all his honest, sluggish guts. We decided that I had come to see Lunacharsky[2] and was just waiting for him in the library.

The clock's melodious tick had erased the German from

99

the room. I was now by myself. Cut-glass spheres blazed
above my head with a yellow silken light. An indescribable
warmth came from the heating pipes. My frozen body
sank into divans which wrapped it in repose.

A superficial search yielded results. In the fireplace I
found a potato pie, a saucepan, a pinch of tea, and some
sugar. And now a spirit lamp was sticking out its little
blue tongue. That night I dined like a human being. I
spread out the finest of napkins on a carved Chinese table
glowing with ancient lacquer. I drank down each piece
of my rough ration bread with sweet, steaming tea whose
coral stars played on the thick sides of the glass. The
velvet of the seat caressed my lean flanks with soft palms.
Outside, fluffy crystals of snow settled on the granite,
deadened by the freezing cold, of St. Petersburg.

Light poured down the warm walls in lemon cascades,
touching the backs of the books, which glimmered bluish-
gold in response.

The books, their pages moldering and scented, carried
me far away to Denmark. More than half a century ago
they had been presented to the young princess as she set
out from her small, sedate country for savage Russia. On
the austere title pages, in three slanting lines of faded ink,
were farewell good wishes from the ladies of the court
who had brought her up; her Copenhagen friends, state
counselors' daughters; her tutors, parchment-faced pro-
fessors from the Lycée; the King, her father, and her
weeping mother, the Queen. On the long shelves were
small, fat books with gold edges now gone dark, ink-
stained children's Bibles with timid blots and awkward,
homemade prayers to the Lord Jesus, small morocco-

bound volumes of Lamartine and Chénier with withered flowers crumbling to dust. I turned over these thin pages, snatched from oblivion; the image of an unknown country, a succession of unusual days passed before me—low walls around the royal gardens, dew on the close-cropped lawns, sleepy emeralds of canals, and the tall King with chocolate-colored sideburns, the quiet ding-dong of a bell over the palace church, and, perhaps, love, a young girl's love— a brief whisper in oppressive halls.

A small woman with powder worked into her skin, a shrewd schemer driven by a tireless urge to exercise authority, a fierce female among the Preobrazhensky Grenadiers, a merciless but attentive mother who met her match in the German woman,[3] the Empress Maria Fyodorovna unfolded before me the scroll of her long, obscure life.

It was very late at night when I tore myself away from this sad and touching chronicle, from all these ghosts with their bloodied heads. The crystal spheres filled with swirling dust were still blazing on the ornate brown ceiling. Leaden trickles of water lay congealed on the blue carpet next to my battered shoes. Tired by the work of my brain, the heat, and the silence, I fell asleep. After midnight I made my way along the dully gleaming corridor to the exit. Alexander III's study was like a high box, its boarded-up windows looking out on the Nevsky. Mikhail Alexandrovich's[4] rooms were the cheerful apartment of a cultured officer who does gymnastics; the walls were covered with a bright material in a pale-pink pattern; on the low mantelpieces there were china knickknacks done in the style of the seventeenth century with its naïveté and excessive fleshiness.

I waited a long time, pressed against a column, until the last court lackey had fallen asleep. His shaven jowls hung down, from long habit, and a lamp threw a faint golden gleam on his high, lolling forehead.

Before one o'clock I was out on the street. The Nevsky took me to its sleepless womb. I went to the Nikolayevsky Station to sleep. Let those who have fled it know that in Petersburg there are places where a homeless poet can spend an evening.

The Chinaman

(1923)

"The Chinaman" (Khodia) *first appeared in the Odessa magazine* Silhouettes, *No. 6–7, in 1923 and subsequently in* The
Pass *(Pereval), No. 6, in 1928. It is published here for the
first time since then.*

The story carries the subtitle "From the book Petersburg
1918." *The resemblance to the subtitle of "An Evening at the
Empress's" ("From a Petersburg Diary") suggests that Babel
had in mind a cycle of Petersburg stories.*

*"The Chinaman" is not the first story by Babel to feature a
prostitute—"Ilya Isaakovich and Margarita Prokofyevna" appeared in 1916. Other stories with a prostitute as protagonist
are "Through the Fanlight" (1923), "My First Fee" (1922–
1928), and "A Hard-Working Woman" (1928), which is included in this book. "The Chinaman" also echoes the following
passage in "The Journey" (1920–1930): "Two Chinamen in
bowler hats, holding loaves of bread under their arms, stood
on the corner of Sadovaya Street. With their frosty nails, they
marked off slivers of the loaf to lure the passing prostitutes.
The women passed by them in a silent procession."**

---

* Isaac Babel, *Lyubka the Cossack and Other Stories.* Andrew R. Mac-
Andrew, trans. (New York: Signet Books, 1963), p. 103. In this collection, the story's title is translated as "The Road There."

The Chinaman

THE NIGHT was merciless and the wind cut to the bone. A dead man's fingers were picking at the frozen entrails of Petersburg. The crimson pharmacies grew cold at the street corners. A druggist sat with his well-groomed head lolling to one side and the frost gripped the purple heart of his pharmacy. And the heart of the pharmacy gasped its last.

There was nobody on Nevsky. Black vials of ink burst in the sky. It was two o'clock in the morning. It was the end. The night was merciless.

A tart and her gentleman friend—two whimpering backs, two frozen crows on a bare bush—were sitting by the railings of the Café Bristol.

". . . If, by the will of Satan, they succeed to the late-lamented Emperor, let them try to get the masses behind them, the matricides. . . . But they won't make it! . . . It's the Latvians who keep them going, and the Latvians are Mongols, Glafira! . . ." The gentleman had drooping jowls, like the sacks of an old-clothes man, and wounded cats prowled in his reddish eyes.

". . . Please, for Christ's sake, Aristarkh Terentyevich, go over to Nadezhdinskaya. Who's going to come up when I'm with a man?"

A Chinese in a leather jacket came by. He raised a loaf of bread above his head and marked off a portion by drawing a line on the crust with his blue fingernail: "A pound."

Glafira held up two fingers: "Two pounds."

A thousand saws whined in the frozen snow of the side streets and a star glinted in the ink-black sky. The Chinese stopped and murmured through clenched teeth: "You dirty, eh?"

"I'm clean, comrade . . ."

A pound it was.

Over on Nadezhdinskaya, Aristarkh's eyes lit up.

"Sweetie," the girl said hoarsely. "I've got my godpapa with me. . . . Mind if he sleeps on the floor?"

The Chinese slowly nodded his head. O, lordly wisdom of the East!

"Aristarkh Terentyevich," the girl called out casually, pressing against a sleek leather shoulder, "my friend says will you come and join us . . ." The gentleman fully regained his spirits.

"He's out of a job for reasons beyond the control of the management," she whispered, wriggling her shoulders, "and his past is nobody's business."

"Exactly. Very pleased to meet you—Sheremetyev is my name."

In the hotel they were given some Chinese vodka, and didn't have to pay for it.

In the early hours the Chinese got out of the bed and melted into the darkness of the room.

"Where you going?" Glafira asked gruffly, kicking up her legs. There was a pool of sweat under her back.

The Chinese went over to Aristarkh, who was snoring

on the floor by the washbasin. He touched the old man's shoulder and motioned him over to Glafira with his eyes.

"Right you are, Johnny," Aristarkh crooned from the floor, "anything you say," and he scurried up to the bed.

"Go away, you dog," Glafira said. "That Chinaman's killed me . . ."

"She won't listen, Johnny," Aristarkh shouted. "You told me to, but she won't listen . . ."

"He my friend," the Chinese said. "He all right, you no-good bitch . . ."

"You're old," the girl whispered, letting the old man into bed, "and what do you know about these things?"

That's the end of the story.

Bagrat-Ogly and the Eyes of His Bull

(1923)

"*Bagrat-Ogly and the Eyes of His Bull*" (Bagrat-Ogly i glaza ego byka) *was first published in 1923 in* Silhouettes, *No. 12, and again in 1924 in* Red Virgin Soil *(*Krasnaya nov*), No. 4. Rediscovered by an Italian scholar, it was published in Italy in 1961* *and in 1967 it appeared in the Tashkent magazine* Star of the Orient *(*Zvezda Vostoka*).*

This story stands in contrast to the rest of Babel's work. It is obviously an experiment under the influence of ornamentalism, a style popular in Russia in the twenties that found its foremost exponents in Andrey Bely and Vsevolod Ivanov. Babel, who otherwise has nothing in common with these writers, here adopts their manner.

"Bagrat-Ogly" has all the marks of ornamentalism, particularly the use of ornate prose to convey an "Oriental" atmosphere. But Babel's preoccupation with senseless cruelty is evident even in this exotic setting.

The story ends on an encounter with "a young mountaineer" who "walked with a free and easy step. The sun rose high above our heads and a sudden peace descended on my wanderer's soul." Might there be more in this yearning for peace and freedom than the romantic frame of the story suggests?

---

* Isaac Babel, *Racconti proibiti e lettere intime* (Milan: Feltrinelli).

Bagrat-Ogly and the Eyes of His Bull

I SAW BY THE WAYSIDE a bull of matchless beauty. Bent over it was a boy, and he was weeping.

"This is Bagrat-Ogly," said a snake charmer who was eating his frugal repast nearby. "Bagrat-Ogly, the son of Kasim."

"He is as beautiful as twelve moons," I said.

"The green mantle of the Prophet," said the snake charmer, "will never envelop the headstrong Kasim. He was much given to litigation and he left his son nothing but a pauper's hovel, his fat wives, and this bull, which had no peer. But Allah is great . . ."

"*Allah il Allah*," I said.

"Allah is great," the old man repeated, thrusting aside his basket of snakes. "The bull grew up and became the mightiest bull in all of Anatolia. Mehmet Khan, a neighbor, stricken with envy, gelded it last night. People will no more bring their cows to Bagrat-Ogly to get them with calf. People will no more pay Bagrat-Ogly a hundred piasters for the love of his bull. He is a beggar, Bagrat-Ogly. He weeps by the wayside."

The stillness of the mountains spread its purple banners

over them. The snows shone on their heights. Blood flowed down the legs of the stricken bull and foamed in the grass. And, hearing the groans of the bull, I looked into his eyes and beheld the death of the bull and my own death, and I fell to the ground in measureless torment.

"Wayfarer," the boy then cried, his face as rosy as the dawn. "You writhe on the ground and there is froth on your lips. A black sickness binds your limbs with the thongs of its convulsions."

"Bagrat-Ogly," I answered him in my affliction, "in the eyes of your bull I saw mirrored the ever-watchful malice of our neighbors, of Mehmet Khan and his like. In their moist depths I saw mirrors in which flared the fires of our neighbors' perfidy—the perfidy of Mehmet Khan and his like. In the eyes of the wounded bull I saw my wasted youth and my manhood forcing a path through the thickets of indifference. In the eyes of your bull, O Bagrat-Ogly, I see the roads, which I have traversed three times, of Syria, Arabia, and Kurdistan, and their flat sands hold no hope for me. The malice of the whole world has entered into the sockets of the eyes of your bull. Flee from the spite of our neighbors, of Mehmet Khan and his like, O Bagrat-Ogly, and let the old snake charmer take up his basket of pythons and flee at your side. . . ."

And, filling the mountain pass with my sighs, I rose to my feet. I breathed in the fragrance of the eucalyptus and went on my way. A many-headed dawn soared over the mountains like a thousand swans. Far away the bay of Trebizond flashed the steel of its waters. And I saw the sea and the yellow gunwales of feluccas. Grass rippled freshly on the ruin of a Byzantine wall. The bazaars of

Trebizond and its carpets arose before me. At a turning of the road to the city I met a young mountaineer. A merlin with a spur of steel sat on his outstretched hand, and he walked with a free and easy step. The sun rose high above our heads and a sudden peace descended on my wanderer's soul.

Grishchuk

(1923)

*In the winter of 1923, some three years after Babel returned
from riding with the Cossacks in the Polish campaign, the
Red Cavalry stories began to appear. (During these three
years, he published the cycle known as the Odessa stories.)
Six of the thirty-six Red Cavalry stories received their first
publication in* The Journal of the Executive Committee of the
Province of Odessa *(Izvestia Odesskogo gubispolkoma), with
the subtitle "From the book* Red Cavalry" *(Konarmiya) and
in the following order: "A Letter," February 11; "The Church
at Novograd," February 18; "Discourse on the* Tachanka,"
*"The Cemetery at Kozin," and "Grishchuk," February 23; "The
Death of Dolgushov," May 1. Of these, "Grishchuk" alone was
never included in any edition of* Red Cavalry; *it was, in fact,
never republished until 1967, when it turned up in the Tashkent magazine* Star of the Orient.

*Grishchuk, the cart driver who appears in both "Discourse
on the* Tachanka" *and "The Death of Dolgushov," is mentioned frequently in the diary Babel kept while he was in the
First Cavalry. Some entries have been quoted by Soviet
scholars in articles on Babel:**

---

* L. Livshits, "Materialy k tvorcheskoi biografii I. Babelia," in
Voprosy literatury, No. 4, 1964, pp. 115–116. I. A. Smirin, op. cit., p. 479.

"July 14, 1920. I have a driver, 39 years old, Grishchuk. Prisoner in Germany for five years, fifty *versts* from home (he is from the Kremenetsk district), they won't let him go, he says nothing."

"July 19, 1920. What is Grishchuk? Eternal silence, limitless apathy. Fifty *versts* from home, hasn't been home in six years, doesn't run away. . . . He knows what authority is, the Germans taught him."

"July 21, 1920. . . . describe Grishchuk."

"July 23, 1920. Grishchuk is fifty *versts* from home. He doesn't run away."

"July 29, 1920. Grishchuk is going home. Sometimes he bursts out, 'I'm tormented.' He could not learn German because his master was stern, they only quarreled, never talked together. One more thing—he nearly starved for seven months because his master gave him practically nothing to eat."

In "Grishchuk," Babel deals with one aspect of this cart driver's obscure past: the time he spent in Germany as a prisoner of war. The artistic problems represented by Grishchuk's submissiveness and passivity are not treated and the characters of both him and his German master remain sketchy. Babel probably felt that he had not done justice to the enigma of Grishchuk's personality as recorded in his notes and for this reason excluded the story from the Red Cavalry cycle.

Grishchuk

THE SECOND TRIP to the *shtetl* ended badly. We had
gone to get forage, and we were returning around
midday. Grishchuk's back peacefully bobbed up and down
in front of my eyes. Just before we got to the village, he
carefully put down the bridle, sighed, and began to slip
from his seat. He slid onto my knees and stretched out
crossways in the cart. His head, growing cold, lolled from
side to side, the horses went at a walking pace, and a
yellowing fabric of repose settled on Grishchuk's face like
a shroud.

"I ain't eaten," he said politely in response to my cry
of alarm, and wearily lowered his eyelids.

This was how we drove into the village—with the driver
stretched out full length in the cart.

At home I fed him bread and potatoes. He ate listlessly,
dozing off all the time and swaying to and fro. Then he
went out into the middle of the yard and, with arms
spread wide, lay down flat on his back.

"You never say anything, Grishchuk," I said frantically.
"How do you expect me to understand, you tiresome fellow?"

He was silent and turned away. And it was only during
the night, as we lay together on the hay to keep each other

warm, that I learned a chapter from the mute tale of his life.

Some Russian prisoners had been used by the Germans to improve their fortifications on the shore of the Baltic sea. When harvest time came, they had been driven inland. Grishchuk had been taken on by a farmer who lived alone and was out of his mind. His madness took the form of keeping total silence. By dint of beating and starving him, he taught Grishchuk to communicate with him in sign language. For four years they lived in silence and peace. Grishchuk didn't learn German because he never heard it. After the German Revolution he set off back to Russia. His master saw him off as far as the edge of the village. They stopped at the highway. The German pointed at the church, at his heart, and at the unending, empty blueness of the horizon. He rested his gray, disheveled, and demented head on Grishchuk's shoulder. They stood like this for a while in a silent embrace. Then the German, throwing up his hands, ran back home with quick, doddering steps.

And Then There Were None

(1923)

"They Were Nine" (Ikh bylo devyat) *is the literal title of this story, which has never been published in the original Russian. The surviving typewritten manuscript carries the date August 1923.*

"And Then There Were None" is related to two entries in the diary Babel kept during the First Cavalry's Polish campaign. In the one dated August 20, 1920, he noted the murder of ten Polish prisoners.* On July 21, 1920, he wrote: "What is our Cossack? Layers of worthlessness, daring, professionalism, revolutionary spirit, bestial cruelty." It is this definition which determines the story's point of view, a view that contrasts with the image of the Cossacks embodied in Red Cavalry. *In these later stories, appalling cruelty is fitted into a heroic framework; the material of the diary has been reexamined and reinterpreted and the Cossacks have acquired legendary stature.*

This shift of emphasis is evident when we compare "And Then There Were None" with "Squadron Commander Trunov," a Red Cavalry *story published in 1925. The entire action of the earlier story became a part of the later, more complicated one. Squadron Commander Trunov is wounded before he interrogates and kills the prisoners, and he dies on the same day while singlehandedly fighting off four airplanes*

---

* This entry is mentioned, but not quoted, by L. Livshits, op. cit., p. 129.

to protect his men. His endurance and courage are as much a part of his nature as the enraged shooting of the unarmed prisoners, whereas in "And Then There Were None" their execution is presented as unqualified murderous injustice.

The narrator of "And Then There Were None" is intimately involved in the events of the story and his reactions are made plain. Perhaps Babel regarded such uninhibited subjectivity as a weakness; perhaps he felt the need of detachment and therefore decided against publishing the story. Whatever his motives might have been, "And Then There Were None" is a lyrical and poignant expression of man's vulnerability and despair.

And Then There Were None

THE PRISONERS ARE DEAD, all nine of them. I feel it in my bones.

Yesterday, when Corporal Golov, a worker from Sormovo, killed the lanky Pole, I said to our staff officer that the corporal was setting a bad example for the men and that we ought to make up a list of the prisoners and send them back for questioning. The staff officer agreed. I got a pencil and paper out of my knapsack and called Golov. He gave me a look of hatred and said, "You look at the world through those spectacles of yours."

"Yes, I do," I replied. "And what do you look at the world through, Golov?"

"I look at it through the dog's life of us workers," he said and, carrying in his hands a Polish uniform with dangling sleeves, he walked back toward one of the prisoners. He had tried it on, and it did not fit him—the sleeves scarcely reached down to his elbows.

Now Golov fingered the prisoner's smart-looking underpants. "You're an officer," Golov said, shielding his face from the sun with one hand.

"No," came the Pole's curt answer.

"The likes of us don't wear that sort of stuff," Golov

muttered and fell silent. He said nothing, quivering as he looked at the prisoner, his eyes blank and wide.

"My mother knitted them," the prisoner said in a firm voice.

I turned around and looked at him. He was a slim-waisted youth with curly sideburns on his sallow cheeks. "My mother knitted them," he said again and looked down.

"She knits like a machine, that mother of yours," Andrushka Burak butted in. Burak is the pink-faced Cossack with silky hair who had pulled the trousers off the lanky Pole as he lay dying. These trousers were now thrown over his saddle. Laughing, Andrushka rode up to Golov, carefully took the uniform out of his hands, threw it over the saddle on top of the trousers, and, with a slight flick of his whip, rode away from us again. At this moment the sun poured out from behind the dark clouds. It cast a dazzling light on Andrushka's horse as it cantered off perkily with carefree movements of its docked tail. Golov looked after the departing Cossack with a bemused expression. He turned around and saw me writing out the list of prisoners. Then he saw the young Pole with his curly sideburns, who glanced at him with the calm disdain of youth and smiled at his confusion. Next, Golov cupped his hands to his mouth and shouted, "This is still a republic, Andrushka! You'll get your share later. Let's have that stuff back."

Andrushka turned a deaf ear. He rode on at a gallop, and his horse swung its tail friskily, just as though it was brushing us off.

"Traitor," Golov said, pronouncing the word very clearly. He looked sulky and his face went stiff. He knelt down on one knee, took aim with his rifle, and fired, but he missed.

Andrushka immediately turned his horse around and charged right up to the corporal. His fresh, pink-cheeked face was angry. "Listen, brother!" he shouted loud and clear and was suddenly pleased by the sound of his own strong voice. "Want to get hurt, you bastard? Why the fuss about finishing off ten Poles? We've killed them off by the hundreds before now without asking your help. Call yourself a worker? Make a job of it, then." And looking at us in triumph, Andrushka galloped off.

Golov did not look up at him. He put his hand to his forehead. Blood was pouring off it like rain off a hayrick. He lay down on his stomach, crawled over to a ditch, and for a long time held his battered, bleeding head in the shallow trickle of water.

The prisoners are dead. I feel it in my bones.

Sitting on my horse, I made a list of them in neat columns. In the first column I numbered them in order, in the second column I gave their names, and in the third the units to which they belonged. It worked out to nine altogether. The fourth was Adolf Shulmeister, a Jewish clerk from Lodz. He kept pressing up to my horse and stroked and caressed my boot with trembling fingers. His leg had been broken with a rifle butt. It left a thin trail of blood like that of a wounded dog, and sweat, glisten-ing in the sun, bubbled on his cracked, yellowish bald pate.

"You are a *Jude*, sir!" he whispered, frantically fondling my stirrup. "You are—" he squealed, the spittle dribbling from his mouth, and his whole body convulsed with joy.

"Get back into line, Shulmeister!" I shouted at the Jew, and suddenly, overcome by a deathly feeling of faintness, I began to slip from the saddle and, choking, I said, "How did you know?"

"You have that nice Jewish look about you," he said in a shrill voice, hopping on one leg and leaving the thin dog's trail behind him. "That nice Jewish look, sir."

His fussing had a sense of death about it, and I had quite a job fending him off. It took me some time to come to, as though I had had a concussion. The staff officer ordered me to see to the machine guns and rode off. The machine guns were being dragged up a hill, like calves on halters. They moved side by side, like one herd, and clanked reassuringly. The sun played on their dusty barrels, and I saw a rainbow on the metal.

The young Pole with the curly sideburns looked at them with peasant curiosity. He leaned right forward, thus giving me a view of Golov as he crawled out of the ditch, weary and pale, with his battered head, and his rifle raised. I stretched out my hand toward him and shouted, but the sound stuck in my throat, to choke and swell there. Golov quickly shot the prisoner in the back of the head and jumped to his feet. The startled Pole swung around to him, turning on his heels as though obeying an order on parade. With the slow movement of a woman giving herself to a man, he raised both hands to the back of his neck, slumped to the ground, and died instantly.

A smile of relief and satisfaction now came over Golov's face. His cheeks quickly regained their color. "*Our* mothers don't knit pants like that for us," he said to me slyly. "Scratch one and give me that list for the other eight."

I gave him the list and said despairingly, "You'll answer for all this, Golov."

"I'll answer for it, all right!" he shouted with indescribable glee. "Not to you, spectacles, but to my own kind, to the people back in Sormovo! They know what's what."

The prisoners are dead. I feel it in my bones.

This morning I decided I must do something in memory of them. Nobody else but me would do this in the Red Cavalry. Our unit has camped in a devastated Polish country estate. I took my diary and went into the flower garden, which was untouched. Hyacinths and blue roses were growing there.

I began to make notes about the corporal and the nine dead men. But I was immediately interrupted by a noise—an all-too-familiar noise. Cherkashin, the staff toady, was plundering the beehives. Mitya, who had pink cheeks and came from Orel, was following him with a smoking torch in his hands. They had wrapped greatcoats around their heads. The slits of their eyes were ablaze. Myriads of bees were trying to fight off their conquerors and were dying by their hives. And I put aside my pen. I was horrified at the great number of memorials still to be written.

Sunset

(1924–1925)

The story "Sunset" (Zakat) was published for the first time in the November 24, 1964, issue of the Moscow weekly Literary Russia, *apparently in honor of the seventieth anniversary of Babel's birth. It was not included, however, in either of the 1966 Soviet editions of his* Collected Works.

The late Soviet scholar L. Livshits wrote the following introduction to accompany the original publication of this story.

In February 1928 the literary magazine *New World (Novy mir)* published I. Babel's play *Sunset,* a sharp and vivid work about Odessa on the eve of World War I (it was reprinted in Babel's *Selected Works,* 1957). [*Sunset was produced in 1929 by the Second Studio of the Moscow Art Theatre. It was a great popular success.*] The play depicts the tragedy of the old proprietor of a moving and hauling business, Mendel Krik, who, like some of Gorky's heroes, is trying to "break out" of his milieu, since he realizes how completely worthless, meaningless, and inhumanly petrified is the world of private property. This hero, already slightly known to readers of Babel's Odessa stories [*which had been published from 1921 to 1924*] as the father of the romantic gangster Benya Krik, who robs the rich and helps the poor, suddenly appears in a new light in the play. And the Moldavanka itself—this suburb of Odessa—is now depicted by Babel not as the exotic town of reckless courage, strength, and passion, but as an assemblage of money-grubbers clinging for all they are worth to the petty-bourgeois way of life.

This radical change in Babel's handling of a theme treated with such brilliance in the Odessa cycle (which immediately gained wide popularity) seemed strange. Only now is it possible to solve this riddle and to understand the path of the writer's evolution.

In the papers of the artist M. Chvanov, eleven pages of close writing—an unknown Babel story, "Sunset"—have been preserved. Unfortunately, a twelfth page with the concluding lines has been lost (Benya Krik's last words have here been supplied from the play *Sunset*). Judging from the handwritten text, Babel worked long and hard at the story in Odessa and Moscow (1924–1925). Babel's notes on the manuscript show that he was trying to overcome colorfulness and exoticism of narrative style and that he was striving for a more realistic and socially significant manner. The mischievously ironical, make-believe world of his Odessa stories—a quirkish, carefree, and outlandish dream of strength and freedom on the part of the weak and the enslaved—acquires new features in the story "Sunset." Here the stagnant petty-bourgeois ways of the Moldavanka are drawn humorously and at the same time in a deliberately lower key, more harshly than in the Odessa cycle. There is now nothing exaltedly colorful and vivid (vivid to the point of absurdity, never drab!) in this life. Everybody is equally bad and nobody arouses sympathy. Benya Krik, the noble bandit, the Odessan Robin Hood, now appears as a crude and resourceful businessman. Hence his conflict with his father. This is how the idea and the style of the future play *Sunset* arose.

Livshits is a little misleading in this commentary. For example, in the play Sunset, *Mendel Krik does not want to "'break out' of his milieu" for the reasons given—he wants to sell his business, leave his wife and children, and go to Bessarabia with his twenty-year-old mistress. If, as Livshits claims, Babel's notes on the manuscript of the story show that he was aiming at "a more realistic and socially significant manner," it cannot be said that he was successful. The story "Sunset" seems as richly textured as anything he ever wrote. Finally, even though Benya has lost his flamboyance since the Odessa stories, "Sunset" cannot be viewed as a study in his social evolution. In doing so, Livshits overlooks the story's ethnic flavor—the Jewishness of the Moldavanka—as well as the universality of its theme, insofar as the story depicts the striving of a new generation determined to replace the old.*

In spite of this critical bias—necessary, perhaps, to get the story published at all—some of Livshits's points are perceptive.

Sunset

ONCE LEVKA, the youngest of the Kriks, saw Lyubka's daughter Tabl. Tabl is the Yiddish for dove. He saw her and left home for three days and nights. The dust of strange sidewalks and the geraniums in strange windows were like balm to his soul. On the third day Levka came home and found his father in the front garden. His father was eating his supper. Madame Gorobchik was sitting next to her husband and looking daggers at the world.

"Go away, ill-mannered lout of a son!" said Papa Krik at the sight of Levka.

"Father," Levka replied, "get your tuning fork and tune up your ears."

"Come to the point."

"There is a girl," said Levka, "with blond hair. She is called Tabl. Tabl is the Yiddish for dove. I have taken a fancy to this girl."

"You have taken a fancy to a slut," said Papa Krik, "and her mother keeps a whorehouse."

Hearing these words of his father, Levka rolled up his sleeves and raised a sacrilegious hand against him. But Madame Gorobchik jumped up from her seat and stood between them.

"Mendel," she howled, "let him have it in the puss! He's eaten up eleven of my meatballs!"

"You have eaten eleven of your mother's meatballs!" Mendel shouted, advancing on his son, but Levka ducked and ran from the yard. His elder brother Benya went along after him. They wandered around the streets till night-time, fomenting like the yeast on which vengeance rises, and at last Levka said to his brother Benya, who a few months later was destined to become Benya the King:

"Benya," he said, "let us pluck up our courage, and people will come and kiss our feet. Let us kill our father, who is no longer called Mendel Krik by the Moldavanka. The Moldavanka calls him Mendel Pogrom. Let us kill our father, because how can we wait any longer?"

"This is not the time," Benya replied. "But the time is coming. Listen for its footsteps and make way for it. Stand aside, Levka."

And Levka stood aside, to make way for time. Time, the old accountant, set out and on its way it met Dvoira, the sister of Benya and Levka; Menashe the driver; and the Russian girl Marusya Yevtushenko.

Ten years ago I still knew people who would have given a lot for Dvoira, the daughter of Mendel Pogrom, but now Dvoira had folds of flesh under her chin, and her eyes were starting out of their sockets. Nobody wanted to have Dvoira. But recently an elderly widower with grown-up daughters had appeared on the scene. He needed a dray and a pair of horses. When she heard about this, Dvoira washed her green dress and hung it out in the yard to dry. She was going to visit the widower to find out how old he was, what sort of horses he wanted, and whether

there was anything in it for her. But Papa Krik had no
time for widowers. He took the green dress, hid it in his
cart, and drove off to work. Dvoira got the flatiron ready
to iron the dress, but she couldn't find it. Then Dvoira fell
on the ground and had a fit. Her brothers dragged her to
the standpipe and poured water on her. Do you recognize the hand of her father, nicknamed Mendel Pogrom?

Then there was Menashe, the old driver, who drove
Lady-in-Waiting and King Solomon. To his own undoing
he learned that old Butsis, Froim Grach, and Chaim
Drong had shoed their horses with rubber. Taking a leaf
out of their book, Menashe went to Pyatirubel and had
King Solomon fitted with rubber shoes. Menashe loved
King Solomon, but old Krik said to him:

"I am not Chaim Drong, and I am not Nicholas the Second, to have my horses prancing about in rubber shoes."

And he grabbed Menashe by the collar, pulled him up
on to his cart, and drove out of the yard. Menashe hung
from his outstretched hand as though from the gallows.
The sunset, a sunset as thick as jam, simmered in the sky;
the bells of Alekseyev Church were moaning, the sun was
sinking behind Blizhniye melnitsy, and Levka ran after
the cart like a dog after his master.

A great crowd followed the two Kriks, as though the
cart was an ambulance, and Menashe just went on hanging from Mendel's hand of iron.

"Father," Levka said to him, "you are crushing my
heart in your outstretched hand. Let it go, let it roll in the
dust."

But Mendel Krik did not even turn round. The horse
galloped on like fury, the wheels thundered, and it was

all like a circus for the crowd. The cart turned into
Dalnitsky Street, where Ivan Pyatirubel had his blacksmith's shop. Mendel rubbed Menashe against the wall of
the blacksmith's shop, and threw him onto a pile of scrap.
Levka ran for a bucket of water and poured it on the old
driver, Menashe. Do you recognize the handiwork of
Mendel, the father of the Kriks, nicknamed Pogrom?

"The time is coming," said Benya once to his brother,
and his brother Levka stood aside to make room for
time. And he was still standing aside when Marusya
Yevtushenko got pregnant.

"Marusya's pregnant," people began to whisper, and
old Krik laughed as he listened to them.

"Marusya's pregnant," he said and laughed like a
child. "Woe be to Israel! Who is this Marusya?"

At this moment Benya came out of the stables and put
his hand on his father's shoulder. "When it comes to
women, I have a heart," Benya said sternly, and he handed
twenty-five rubles to his father, because he wanted
Marusya's abortion to be done by a doctor in a clinic and
not in Marusya's home.

"I will give her this money," said old Krik, "and she
will have an abortion, or else I'll never have any peace of
mind."

And the next morning he went off on his usual round
with Burglar and Darling Wife, and around midday
Marusya Yevtushenko came to the Kriks' house. "Benchik," she said, "I loved you, damn your eyes!" And she
threw ten rubles into his face. Two five-ruble notes
never came to more than ten. It was then that Benchik
said "Let's kill father" to his brother Levka, and they sat

down on a bench by the gate, and next to them sat
Semyon, Anisim the watchman's son, who was seven
years old. And who would have thought that this seven-
year-old pipsqueak was already capable of love and
hatred? Who would have thought that it loved Mendel
Krik? Yet it did.

The brothers sat on the bench and tried to figure how
old their father was, how much over sixty he might be,
and Semyon, the son of Anisim the watchman, sat next to
them.

At that hour the sun had not yet reached Blizhniye
melnitsy. Its light was gushing into the black clouds like
blood from a disemboweled hog, and the drays of old
Butsis rumbled through the streets on their way home
from work. The dairy maids were milking the cows for
the third time, and Madame Parabellum's girls were hauling pails of warm evening milk up the steps to her. And
Madame Parabellum was standing at the top of the steps,
clapping her hands:

"Come along, girls—mine and all you others!" she
shouted. "Berta Ivanovna, all you ice-cream and yoghurt
makers! Come and get your evening milk."

Berta Ivanovna, the German teacher, who got two
quarts of milk per lesson, was the first to be served. After
her, Dvoira Krik came up to see how much water Madame
Parabellum had put in her milk, and how much soda had
gone into it too. Benchik took his sister aside:

"This evening," he said, "when you see the old man
killing us, go up to him and bash his brains in with the
colander. And let that be the end of the firm Mendel Krik
and Sons."

"Amen, and good luck to you," Dvoira replied and went out of the gate. The good people of the Moldavanka came in hordes, as though there was a game going on in the Kriks' yard. They streamed in, as they throng to the Market Square on the second day of Passover. Pyatirubel the blacksmith brought along his pregnant daughter-in-law and his grandchildren. Old Butsis came with his niece who had just arrived from Kamenets-Podolski. Tabl came with a Russian. She leaned on his arm and played with a ribbon in her braids. Last on the scene was Lyubka, who galloped up on his roan stallion. Only Froim Grach came all by himself, as red as rust, one-eyed, and in a coat made of sailcloth.

People sat down in the front garden and took out things to eat. The factory hands removed their shoes, sent their children for beer, and laid their heads on their wives' bellies. And then Levka said to Benchik, his brother:

"Mendel Pogrom is our father," he said, "and Madame Gorobchik is our mother, and people are dogs, Benchik. We are working for dogs."

"We ought to think," Benchik replied, but the words were hardly out of his mouth when there was a sound like a thunderclap in Golovkovskaya Street. The sun shot upward and began to spin like a red cup on the point of a spear. The old man's dray careered up to the gate. Darling Wife was covered in lather, and Burglar was bursting from his harness. The old man flourished his whip over the two crazed horses. His huge legs were spread wide, a purple sweat simmered on his face, and he was singing in a drunken voice. And at this moment Semyon, the son of

Anisim, slipped like a snake past somebody's legs, darted out into the street, and shouted at the top of his voice:

"Get back, Mister Krik, your sons are going to beat you . . ." But it was too late. Father Krik hurtled into the yard on his foam-covered horses. He raised his whip, opened his mouth . . . and was struck dumb. The people sitting in the garden looked at him goggle-eyed. Benchik stood on the left by the dovecote. Levka stood on the right by the watchman's hut.

"Just look, people," said Mendel in a faint voice, lowering his whip, "how my own flesh and blood are raising their hands against me."

And, jumping down from the carriage, the old man went for Benya and hit him on the bridge of the nose with his fist. Levka ran to the rescue and did something to his father's face that was like shuffling a new deck of cards. But the old man had a hide like the devil's, and the stitches in it were made of cast iron. He twisted Levka's arms and threw him on the ground next to his brother. He sat on Levka's chest and the women closed their eyes so as not to see the old man's broken teeth and his face covered in blood. And at this moment the people of the unbelievable Moldavanka heard the quick steps of Dvoira and her voice saying:

"This is for Levka, for Benchik, and for me, Dvoira, and for everybody else," and she smashed her father's head with the colander. People jumped up and ran to them, waving their arms. They dragged the old man over to the standpipe, as Dvoira had once been dragged there, and turned on the water. Blood flowed down the drain like water, and the water flowed like blood. Madame Gorobchik pushed her way through the crowd and came up, hopping like a sparrow.

"Don't be so quiet, Mendel," she whispered. "Say something, Mendel . . ." But hearing the silence in the yard, seeing that the old man had come from work, that the horses had not been unharnessed and nobody was pouring water on the overheated wheels, she ran away across the yard, like a dog with three legs. And then the worthy citizens moved closer. Old man Krik was lying with his beard in the air.

"Curtains," said Froim Grach and turned away.

"It's all over," said Chaim Drong, but Pyatirubel the blacksmith wagged his forefinger under Chaim Drong's nose:

"Three against one," said Pyatirubel. "What a disgrace for the Moldavanka. But it's not night yet. I've still to see the man who could finish off old Krik . . ."

"It *is* night," interrupted Arye Leib, who had suddenly appeared from nowhere. "It *is* night, Ivan Pyatirubel. Trust a Russian to say no when life is crying out yes."

And squatting down by the old man, Arye Leib wiped his lips with a handkerchief, kissed him on the forehead, and told him about King David, the King of the Jews, who had many wives and was rich in land and treasure, and who always knew when it was time to cry.

"Don't whine, Arye Leib," Chaim Drong shouted at him and began to poke him in the back. "That's enough of your funeral service, you're not at the cemetery now!"

And turning to old Krik, Chaim Drong said:

"Get up, old driver, have a drink of water and give us a piece of your mind, the way you always do, you coarse

old bastard, and let's have a pair of drays in the morning,
I've got a pile of scrap . . ."

And everybody waited to hear what Mendel would say
about the drays. But for a long time he said nothing, then
he opened eyes and, after that, his mouth, which was covered with dirt and hairs; blood oozed through his lips.

"I don't have any drays," said old Krik. "My sons have
done me in. My sons must take over."

They were not to be envied, those who took over the
bitter legacy of Mendel Krik. How could they be envied,
when all the feed racks in the stables had rotted away a
long time ago and half the wheels on the drays were worn
out? The sign above the gate was a mess—you couldn't
make out a single word—and none of the drivers had a
decent change of underwear. Half the town owed money
to Mendel Krik, but his horses were so hungry they licked
the figures chalked up on the wall as they took oats from
the feed racks.

The whole day long, peasants came to Mendel's bewildered heirs and demanded payment for straw and bar-
ley. The whole day long, women came to take gold rings
and nickel-plated samovars out of pawn. There was no
more peace in the house of the Kriks, but Benya, who in a
few months' time was to become Benya the King, was not
downhearted and he ordered a new sign: "Mendel Krik
and Sons, Movers and Haulers." This was to be painted
in gold letters on a pale-blue background with intertwined
bronze-colored horseshoes. He also bought a length of
ticking to make underpants for the drivers, and some tim-
ber—unheard-of till now—to repair the drays. He hired
Pyatirubel for a whole week and started giving receipts
to the customers. And by the evening of the next day

he was more worn out than if he had made fifteen trips between Odessa-Port and Odessa-Freight. And in the evening he found not one crumb of bread and not one clean plate in the whole house. Now you can really get an idea of the depths of Madame Gorobchik's callousness. Trash lay unswept in the rooms; some delicious jellied calves' heels had been thrown out for the dogs. And Madame Gorobchik herself was perched by her husband's bed like a crow in an autumn tree after slops have been thrown over it.

"Just get an eyeful of those two," said Benya to his younger brother. "Look at them under your microscope, this pair of lovebirds, because I've got an idea they're up to something."

Thus spoke Benchik, who could see right through people with the eyes of Benya the King, to his brother Levka, but Levka the greenhorn didn't believe him and went to bed. The old man was already snoring on his wooden bed, and Madame Gorobchik was tossing and turning from side to side. She kept spitting on the wall and the floor. She was so bad-tempered she couldn't sleep. But at last she dropped off too. Stars—green stars on a dark-blue background—were scattered in front of the window like soldiers relieving themselves. Just across the way, at Petka Ovsyanitsa's, a phonograph started playing Jewish songs, but then it stopped. The night was attending to its business and the air, the rich air, poured into the window of Levka, the youngest of the Kriks. He liked the air, Levka did. He lay there and breathed, and slept and reveled in the air. He felt on top of the world until the moment when a rustling and creaking sound came from his father's bed.

Then Levka closed his eyes and got his ears into position.
Papa Krik lifted up his head like a mouse sniffing the air
and crept down from the bed. The old man pulled a bag
of money out from under his pillow and slung his boots
over his shoulder. Levka didn't stop him, because where
could he go, the old dog? Then he slipped out after his
father and saw Benya edging his way along the wall from
the other side of the yard. The old man sneaked silently
over to where the carriages were parked and whistled to
the horses, and the horses came up to nuzzle against
Mendel's head. It was night in the yard, a night blanketed
with stars, dark-blue air, and silence.

"Sh . . ." Levka put his finger to his lips, and so did
Benchik, who was closing in from the other side of the
yard. The old man whistled to the horses as though they
were little children, then he ran between the drays and
made water in the gateway.

"Anisim," he said in a low voice and rapped on the window of the watchman's hut. "Anisim, my friend, open the
gate."

Anisim came out of his hut as disheveled as hay.

"Boss," he said, "I beg and pray you—don't demean
yourself before the likes of me. Go back to bed, boss . . ."

"You'll open up the gate for me," the old man said even
more softly. "I know you will, Anisim my friend . . ."

"Get back inside," said Benchik at this moment, coming
up to the hut and putting his hand on his father's shoulder. And then, right in front of him, Anisim saw Mendel
Krik's face, which was as white as paper, and he turned
away so as not to see his boss's face like this.

"Don't hit me, Benchik," said old Krik, backing away.

"How much longer does your father have to suffer?"

"Oh, lowdown father," Benchik replied, "how can you talk like that?"

"And why not?" Mendel shouted and struck himself on the head with his fist. "And why not, Benchik?" he shouted at the top of his voice and began to sway as though he was going to have a fit. "Look at this yard where I have lived half my life. It has seen me, this yard, as the father of my children, as the husband of my wife, as the master of my horses. It has seen me in my glory, it has seen my twenty stallions and my twelve drays with their iron wheels. It has seen my legs as firm as tree trunks and my hands, my cruel hands. And now, my dear sons, open the gate for me, and let me have my way today, let me leave this yard which has seen too much . . ."

"Father," Benchik replied, without looking up, "go back to your wife."

But he didn't have to go back to Madame Gorobchik: she came running to the gate herself and went down on the ground, kicking her old yellow legs in the air.

"Ai," she wailed, rolling on the ground, "Mendel Krik and my sons, my bastards . . . What have you done to me, my bastards, what have you done with the hair on my head, what have you done with my poor old body, where are they, my teeth? Where is my youth? . . ."

The old woman howled, tried to tear her nightshift from her back, and, getting to her feet, began to turn round and round on the spot, like a dog trying to bite its tail. She scratched her sons' faces, kissed them, and dug her nails into their cheeks.

"You old thief!" Madame Gorobchik sobbed, and she

pranced around Mendel, pulling and tweaking his mustache. "You old thief, my old Mendel . . ."

All the neighbors had been wakened by her yelling, everybody in the yard had run up to the gate, and barebellied children began to tootle on pipes. The whole of the Moldavanka thronged in to see the commotion. And Benya Krik, whose hair went gray from shame on the spot, barely managed to drive the "lovebirds" back into the house. He scattered the crowd with a stick and drove them back to the gate, but Levka, his younger brother, took hold of him by the collar and began to shake him like a pear tree:

"Benchik," he said, "we are tormenting the old man. . . . It makes me cry, Benchik . . ."

"It makes you cry, does it," Benchik replied, and collecting all the spittle in his mouth, he spat in Levka's face. "Oh, lowdown brother," he whispered, "vile brother, free my hands and don't get in my way."

And Levka freed his hands. He slept in the stable till dawn, and then he left the house. The dust of strange sidewalks and the geraniums in strange windows brought him comfort. He trod the paths of sorrow for two days and two nights, and when he returned on the third day he saw a blue sign blazing above the house of the Kriks. The blue sign made his heart miss a beat, and his eyes went head over heels at the sight of the velvet tablecloths spread on tables and the great crowd of guests laughing in the front garden. Dvoira was walking among the guests in a white headdress, women in starched clothes sat in the grass like white enamel teapots, and some lanky factory hands, who had already managed to get rid of their jackets, took hold of Levka and pushed him inside the house. Here, with his face all cut up, sat Mendel Krik, the oldest of the Kriks. Asher Boyarsky, owner of the firm "Chef d'oeuvre," the hunchbacked tailor Efim, and Benya Krik were dancing attendance on the disfigured old man.

"Efim," said Asher Boyarsky to his tailor, "do us a favor. Bend down a little closer and measure Monsieur Krik for one of our de luxe striped suits, as if it was for one of us, and make so bold as to inquire what sort of material his honor was thinking of—English double-breasted navy, English single-breasted army, Polish demi-saison, or Moscow serge . . ."

"What sort of a suit do you want?" Benchik then asked his father. "Just let Monsieur Boyarsky in on the secret."

"Make your father a suit," old Krik answered, wiping away a tear, "to match your feelings for him."

"Since Papa isn't a naval man," Benya said before he could finish, "the army stuff will be the most suitable. Make him a suit for every day of the week, to begin with."

Monsieur Boyarsky bent forward and cocked an ear: "Tell me what you mean," he said.

"What I mean," Benya replied, "is that here is a Jew who has gone all his life ragged, barefoot, and caked in mud like a convict on the island of Sakhalin . . . and now that, thanks to God, he has entered his ripe old years, we must put an end to this convict's life, we must make every Sabbath into a real Sabbath . . ."

A Hard-Working Woman

(1928)

"A Hard-Working Woman" (Staratelnaya zhenshchina) *originally appeared in the Soviet literary miscellany* The Pass, *No. 6, in 1928. This is its first publication since then.*

"The Chinaman" and "Through the Fanlight" were also published—both for the second time—in the same issue of The Pass. *All three stories deal with prostitution.*

"A Hard-Working Woman" is set among the partisans of Makhno,* whose name and exploits are mentioned in several of the Red Cavalry stories. In "Squadron Commander Trunov," for example, we hear of a man whose "name was Seliverstov. Once he had deserted Makhno and now he was serving in our Thirty-third Regiment." Perhaps "A Hard-Working Woman" was inspired by an account Babel heard from someone who had been with Makhno before joining the First Cavalry.

It is likely that this story was written a number of years before it was published. The theme of prostitution in a war setting recalls Babel's stories of the early twenties; and the narrator, who abstains from judging except for a final comment of horror mingled with admiration, is reminiscent of Lyutov, the narrator of Red Cavalry.

---

* Nestor Ivanovich Makhno (1884–1935), a Ukrainian who called himself a "Communist-anarchist," led a band of partisans that fought both the Whites and the Reds during the Civil War. His headquarters were in Gulyai-polye in the Ukraine, mentioned in this story. Makhno had a reputation for brutality. In 1919 his band was destroyed and he fled to Paris, where he lived until his death.

A Hard-Working Woman

THREE OF MAKHNO'S MEN—Gniloshkurov and two others—had reached an agreement with a woman concerning the performance of certain amorous services. For two pounds of sugar she had undertaken to receive all three of them, but with the third she couldn't stand it any more and started hopping round the room. She bolted into the yard, and in the yard she ran into Makhno. Makhno brought her down with his long whip and cut open her upper lip. Gniloshkurov got a taste of it too.

This had happened at nine o'clock in the morning; then the whole of the day was taken up by all kinds of chores, and now it was night and rain was falling, a light, whispering, relentless rain. It murmured away outside, and in front of me a lone star hung in the window. Kamenka was sunk in darkness; the ghetto was alive with teeming darkness in which the coming and going of Makhno's men never ceased. Somebody's horse whinnied shrilly, like a woman pining for her lover, sleepless *tachanki*[1] creaked at the edge of town and the boom of big guns, dying away, settled down for the night on the wet black earth. And only the ataman's window was ablaze in a distant street. Like a searchlight, its beam probed triumphantly into the poverty of the autumn night and shimmered in the drenching rain. Inside, in Makhno's headquarters, a brass band was playing in honor of Antonina Vasilyevna, a nurse who was spending her first night with the ataman. The blare of the fat, doleful trumpets got louder and louder, and the partisans huddling under my window listened to the thunderous strains of old marching songs. The three of them—Gniloshkurov and his two pals—were sitting out there. A little while later, Kikin, a wild Cossack youth, rolled up to them. He kicked his legs in the air, stood on his hands, sang and hooted, and then had trouble calming down, as though he'd had a fit. "Ovsyanitsa," Gniloshurov whispered suddenly. "Ovsyanitsa," he said dejectedly. "I just don't get it: she laid a couple more after me, and everything was right as rain . . . And when I was doing up my pants, she says such nice things to me— 'you're getting on a little,' she says, 'thanks for your company, I like you,' she says. . . . 'Anelya they call me,' she says. 'Anelya's my name.' . . . So how I figure it, Ovsyanitsa, she must have eaten some nasty herb early in the morning, and then, to make things worse, Petka comes along too . . ."

"Petka comes along," said the fifteen-year-old Kikin, squatting down and lighting a cigarette. " 'Have a heart, man,' she says to Petka, 'I've got no strength left,' and up she jumps and starts spinning round like a top, and the boys put out their hands to stop her going out the door, but she carries on like crazy . . ." Kikin got up, his eyes shone and he guffawed. "And she runs out, and who should be standing at the door but Makhno . . . 'Stop,' he says. 'I bet you've got the pox, I'll carve you up, I will.'

And he downs her with his whip, and she looks as if she's going to let him have a piece of her mind . . ."

"There's no denying," Petka Orlov butted in, interrupting Kikin in his soft, wistful voice, "there's no denying that some people are greedy, real greedy . . . I told her: 'There's three of us, Anelya,' I said. 'Find a girl friend, give her some of the sugar, and she'll help you out . . .' 'No,' says she, 'I'm sure I'll manage by myself, I've got three children to feed, it's not as if I was a schoolgirl or something . . .' "

"She's a hard-working woman," Gniloshkurov assured Petka, still sitting under my window, "as hard-working as they make 'em." . . . He said no more. I again heard the noise of running water. As before, the rain purred and sang and sighed on the rooftops. The wind was now catching it up and driving it sideways. The exultant blare of the trumpets had died away in Makhno's house and the light in his window had dimmed to half its former strength. Gniloshkurov now got up from his bench and blacked out with his body the dull glimmer of the moon. He yawned, tucked in his shirt, scratched his belly, which was unusually white, and went into the shed to sleep. The soft voice of Petka Orlov floated after him:

"Back in Gulyai-polye," Petka was saying, "we had a fellow called Ivan Golub—he wasn't from our parts. He was the quiet sort, didn't drink and liked his work. He took on too much and killed himself with it . . . People were sorry for him and the whole village turned out for his funeral, even though he was a stranger." And going right up to the door of the shed, Petka went on, dropping his voice even lower and putting more and more feeling

into it, about the dead Ivan. "Some people have no heart,"
Gniloshkurov replied as he fell asleep. "They really
haven't, believe me . . ."

Gniloshkurov went to sleep and so did the two others.
And only I was left by the window. My eyes probed the
silent night, I was gnawed by the wild beast of memory,
and sleep would not come.

. . . She sat from early morning in the main street selling berries. Makhno's men paid her in worthless bank-
notes. She was a full-bodied, lightly built blonde. Gniloshkurov, his belly stuck out, was sunning himself on his
bench. He dozed and waited, and the woman, in a hurry
to sell off her wares, gazed at him with her dark-blue eyes,
and her face was slowly covered by a gentle flush.

"Anelya," I whispered her name. "Anelya."

The Jewess

(1934?)

The Russian text of "The Jewess" has never been published. Although the typewritten manuscript in our possession is incomplete, Babel's architecture is so solid that the story has artistic unity just as it stands.

The structure of "The Jewess"—different from that of Babel's other known fiction—and the fact that he was working on it in the early thirties when he had expressed an urge to experiment with larger forms, make it seem likely that "The Jewess" was conceived as a novel.

The story is autobiographical insofar as it relates to the death of Babel's father in 1923. But it should not be read as a straightforward family reminiscence. In the first place Babel, unlike his fictional hero, was actually present when his father died. Also, Babel's family lived in Odessa, where he and his mother were born; the family in the story lives in the Pale of Settlement. Instead of the robust characters of Odessa, "The Jewess" shows us a devastated shtetl *peopled by broken-down and desperate Jews, much like the ghetto dwellers of Galicia depicted in* Red Cavalry.

Babel made the following notes on the manuscript:

Eternal Jew?
More dialogue, less pathetic narration?
Style of Gleb Alekseyev?

Strengthen the factual side—surnames, names, descriptions of
the place?
Factual description of the cemetery?

*These notes suggest that he was consciously aiming at a new
style. In "The Jewess" there is a noticeable reduction in the
ornamentation of narrative so characteristic of his earlier work
and a turn toward direct descriptive realism. (This may explain the reference to Gleb Alekseyev [1892–   ], a "physio-
logical" writer who portrayed social types through descriptions
of manners and mores.) There is no distancing through the
eyes of a sensitive and compassionate narrator, no softening of
the brutality. Babel finally achieves the "objectivity" for which
he had always striven.*

*The notes also throw light on what appears to be the main
point of the story—the impossibility of escaping from one's
Jewishness, from one's own character, from one's historical circumstances. In Babel's earlier Odessa stories the action springs
from the will of the characters—society is presumed to be static
and outside history. In the Red Cavalry stories the dynamic is
men's will in history—their true natures are brought out by the
ordeal of war. In "The Jewess," however, the dramatic focus
lies in the struggle of man against history—of man trying to
re-create an identity by finding a new relation to the forces of
social change. Hence Boris does not allow his mother and sister
to mourn the old way of life. Instead, he tries to integrate them
into a new world. He understands that history has passed
them by and that they are condemned—left to themselves they
will find no way out. He believes he will be able to put his
heritage to the service of the new order and to act as a link between generations. The paradox is that for this to take place
the new world must accept the new Jew. Yet if the new world
were to reject him, what choices would be left to such a man
as Boris?*

"The Jewess," then, is not a romanticized personal chronicle but an attempt to assess an irreversible social transformation. The surviving manuscript of the story has obscure words and passages, variants, and question marks between brackets. It breaks off in the middle of the fifth line of the sixth section. Since this text seems to require only stylistic polishing, the main question is: Why did Babel leave "The Jewess" unfinished? Why did he abandon a work that shows such mastery of craft, originality of conception, and a development toward a different view of the world? If "The Jewess" was conceived as a novel, as I believe it was, did Babel feel that he could not meet the requirements of the larger form? Was it fear of what would become of Boris if the story continued with the unflinching truthfulness of the opening sections? Was Babel unable to resolve in himself a conflict he hoped to portray in Boris? Was it because he, so much like Boris in the story, found himself confronted by a choice between alienation and concession, capitulation and death? Or do we have only an incomplete variant of a manuscript that had been completed but that disappeared when Babel's papers were seized at the time of his arrest?

The Jewess

I N ACCORDANCE WITH CUSTOM, the old woman lay on a bench for seven days. On the eighth day, she got up and went outside into the *shtetl*. The weather couldn't have been better. In front of the house stood a chestnut tree, its candles already lit. It was bathed in sunlight. When you think of people who have just died on a beautiful sunny day, life seems merciless and its troubles beyond repair. The old woman was wearing an old-fashioned black silk dress with a pattern of black printed flowers, and a silk kerchief. She had dressed up like this for the sake of her dead husband, so that the neighbors shouldn't think that he or she had lost pride in the face of death.

In this dress, old Esther Erlich went to the cemetery. The flowers thrown on the mound of earth by the grave had shriveled. She touched them with her fingers, and they began to drop down and fall apart. Old Alter, who was always in attendance at the cemetery, ran up to her. "For the service, Madame Erlich." She opened her handbag, slowly counted her money, a few silver coins, and handed them silently to Alter, who was put out by her silence. He walked away on his bandy legs, muttering to himself. The sun followed his faded, misshapen back. She was left alone at the graveside. The wind blew through the treetops and bent them over.

"I feel very bad without you, Marius," said the little old lady. "I cannot tell you how bad." She sat by the grave, clutching some bedraggled flowers in her wrinkled hands. She clenched her hands till they hurt, trying to drive away her memories. It is terrible for a wife to sit by her husband's grave and look back on thirty-five years of her life, on all the days and nights of her marriage. Worn out by the struggle with her memories, she trudged back home in the evening through the squalid streets of the *shtetl*.

Yellow sunlight lay over the marketplace. Deformed old men and women were selling sunflower oil, withered onions, small fish, and candies for children. Esther was met at the door of her house by her fifteen-year-old daughter. "Mama," she cried in that peculiarly despairing way that Jewish women have, "don't make things hard—Boris is here."

Fidgeting with his hands, her son stood in the doorway in his military uniform, with medals on his chest. The broken old woman, her face flushed and tear-stained, stopped in front of him. "How dare you be late at your father's deathbed? How could you do this to him?"

Her son and daughter led her inside by the arm. There, in the room where she had lain for seven days, she sat down and, looking her son straight in the face, began to torture him with the story of his father's death. It was a circumstantial account, in which nothing was left out— the swelling of his legs, the way his nose had turned blue on the morning of the day he died, the frantic dash to the pharmacy for oxygen, the unfeelingness of the people around his deathbed. Nor did she fail to mention how he had called for his son as he lay dying. She had gone down on her knees and tried to warm his hand in hers. He had pressed her hand feebly as he repeated his son's name over and over again. Rolling his glazed eyes, he went on for a long time, distinctly pronouncing his name—the word "Boris" droned in the deathly hush of the room like a spinning wheel. Then at last the old man had gasped for breath and said in a choking voice, "Borechka." His eyes started from their sockets, and he wailed and moaned, "Borechka." The old woman, holding his hand in hers, had said, "I am here. This is your son." The hand of the dying man came alive with new strength; it began to jerk and claw at the hands that were warming it. He began to shout, "Borechka!" in a quite different tone, a kind of high-pitched voice in which he had never before spoken during the whole of his life, and he died with this name on his lips.

"How could you be late?" the old woman said to her son, who was sitting sideways at the table. They had not lit the lamp. Boris sat in the dark, which shrouded the room. Nothing stirred. He could hear the angry breathing of his mother. He got up, catching his revolver against the table's edge, and went outside. For half the night he walked round the *shtetl* in which he had been born. Reflected in the river, the stars quivered pure and snakelike. A foul smell came from the hovels at the water's edge. There were gaping holes in the walls of the synagogue, which three hundred years earlier had withstood Khmelnitsky's marauding troops. His native *shtetl* was dying. The new era was ringing the knell of its defenseless way of life. "Is it the end or a new beginning?" Boris asked himself. He was so sick at heart that he hadn't the strength to ponder this question. The school he had once attended had been destroyed by Hetman Struk[1] in 1919. The house

in which his friend Zhenya had once lived was now the
Labor Exchange. He walked past ruins, past the sleeping,
squat, and lopsided houses with the stench of poverty
seeping out of their doorways, and said goodbye to them.
When he got home, his mother and sister were still sitting up waiting for him. The samovar, which needed
cleaning, was boiling on the table. There was also a piece
of chicken. Esther came up to him on her unsteady legs,
pressed her body against his, and began to cry. Through
her dress, through her loose and flaccid skin, he could feel
the beating of her heart, and the beating of his own
heart—they were one and the same. The smell of his
mother's quivering flesh was so bitter and sad that he was
overcome with unutterable pity for this heart, the heart of
the Erlichs. The old woman wept, shaking on his breast
decorated with the two orders of the Red Banner. They
were wet with tears.

This was the beginning of her recovery, and of her sub-
mission to loneliness and death.

II

The relatives arrived the next morning. They were the
remnants of a large and ancient family, which numbered
among its members merchants, adventurers, and timid,
poetic revolutionaries from the heyday of The People's
Will[2] terrorist organization. Boris's aunt was a nurse who
had done her training in Paris on twenty rubles a month,
and had once listened to the speeches of Jaurès and
Guesde.[3] One of his uncles was a pathetic ne'er-do-well
shtetl philosopher. His other uncles had been grain dealers,
traveling salesmen, or shopkeepers who had now lost their

livelihood—a motley crowd of pathetic, sweating people in rust-colored raincoats or capes. They told Boris once more how his father's legs had swollen, where he had developed bedsores, and who had run to the druggist for oxygen. One of the grain merchants, who had been a rich man in his day but had now been driven out of his house and wrapped his skinny old legs in soldier's leggings, took Boris to one side. He wanted to get on closer terms with this nephew who had strayed so far from the rest of the family. Looking at him with blinking eyes, he said that he had not expected the dead man's body to be so clean and smooth. He had seen it while they were washing him, and he had been as well turned out and clean-cut as a boy. And to think that just because of some wretched valve in the heart or a tiny vein . . . As Boris's uncle said this, he was probably thinking that he was born of the same mother as the dead man, and that he, too, must have exactly the same sort of valve in his heart as his brother who had died a week ago.

The next day Boris was asked, at first timidly and then with a convulsiveness born of long-suppressed despair, whether he could recommend his uncles for membership in a trade union. Because of their status under the old regime, none of the Erlichs had so far been admitted to a trade union.

The life of these old people was unutterably sad. Their houses were falling down and the roofs leaked; they had sold everything, even their wardrobes, and nobody would give them work. But they had to pay for their rooms and water at the same rate as self-employed people. On top of it all, they were old and suffering from awful complaints —the forerunners of cancer and other wasting diseases—

like all old Jewish families when they are in decline. Boris
had long believed that it was right to put people out of
their misery, but now his mother was here at his side, her
face so much like his face, her body so like what his would
be in a couple of decades that he suddenly had a sense of
the common lot of all their bodies—the bodies of all the
Erlichs, which were all in some way bound up with each
other. He overcame his scruples and went to the chairman
of the local soviet. This chairman was a Petersburg worker
who seemed to have been waiting all his life for an opportunity to tell somebody how wretched it was to work
in a local soviet in this lousy former so-called Pale of
Jewish Settlement, how difficult it was to get these *shtetls*
back on their feet and lay the foundations for a new and
better life in these lousy Jewish towns of the godforsaken
southwestern provinces, which were dirt poor and dying
a dog's death. For several days afterward, Boris had to face
both the cemetery of his native *shtetl* and the imploring
eyes of his uncles who had once been happy-go-lucky
traveling salesmen and now thought only of joining a
trade union or getting registered at the Labor Exchange.

   During these few days, the Indian summer came to an
end and autumn set in. It began to rain the cold *shtetl* rain
that brought mud and pebbles—a mixture like concrete—
down from the hills. The entrance to the house was flooded
with water. They put rusty tins and Passover saucepans
under cracks in the ceiling. As you walked about the room,
you had to watch your step so as not to put your foot in
one of them.

   It was then that Boris said to his mother, "Let's clear
out."

"Where to?"

"To Moscow, Mother."

"Aren't there enough Jews in Moscow already, without us?"

"Nonsense," said Boris. "Don't listen to what people say."

She sat in her corner in the leaking front room, by the window from which she could see the potholed sidewalk, the neighbor's tumbledown house, and the last thirty-five years of her life. Sitting there, she commiserated, with all the feeling of which she was capable, with her sisters, brothers-in-law, and nephews, to none of whom fate had granted a son like hers. She had expected that Boris would sooner or later talk of Moscow, and she knew that she would give in to him. But before this she wanted to give full rein to her own distressed feelings and steep her surrender in the anguish of the whole neighborhood. She said that she would be terribly unhappy traveling alone, without her husband, whose great dream had been to go to Moscow, to leave this godforsaken place and live out the rest of his days—days from which one expects no more than peace and the sight of other people's happiness—in the new promised land, together with his son. But he was lying in his grave, under the rain that had been lashing down all night, and she would go to Moscow, where, it was said, people were happy, carefree, high-spirited, full of plans, and doing all kinds of remarkable things. Esther said it would be hard for her to leave all these graves where their ancestors—rabbis, *tsadiks,* and Talmud scholars—lay under gray, time-hallowed stones. She would never see them again, and how would he, her son, answer for her when the time came for her to die in strange parts, among people so utterly foreign to her that she could not even picture them to herself? And then, how would she ever be able to forgive herself if she should actually *like* the life in Moscow? As she figured out just how unbearable it would be for her to feel happy at such a time, her hands, their long fingers deformed by rheumatism, trembled and went moist, and the veins on her yellow breast swelled up and throbbed terribly. The rain beat down on the corrugated-iron roof. For the second time since the arrival of her son, the little old Jewess in the elastic-sided shoes began to cry. She agreed to go to Moscow, because there was nowhere else for her to go, and also because her son was so much like his father that she could not be parted from him; like everybody else, her husband had had his faults and his pathetic little secrets, about which only she knew, but would never tell.

III

The only argument was over the question of what to take with them. Esther wanted to take everything, while Boris insisted that they should get rid of the lot and sell it. But there was nobody in Kremenets to sell it to. There was no demand for furniture, and the local dealers, who looked like undertakers and had sprung up from God knows where, like visitors from another world, were vicious characters who would offer almost nothing, whining that they could only hope to sell to the peasants.

But the relatives helped them out. As soon as they got over the first shock of their bereavement, they began to steal the dead man's things for all they were worth. And since at heart most of them were honest people, not out for petty gain, the spectacle of this furtive pilfering was particularly sad. Esther, quite bewildered and her face flushed, made one feeble attempt to seize an outstretched hand, but the hand trembled so much, and was so clammy, wrinkled, and old, with its edging of broken nails, that she recoiled, understanding everything in a flash, aghast both at the thought that anyone should want to prevent this painful larceny and that people with whom she had grown up should rush to take cupboards and sheets from her house like this.

All her things were being forwarded express to Moscow. The relatives wept as they helped her tie the bundles she was taking with her. They had now come to their senses, and, sitting on the bundles, they talked about how they were staying in Kremenets and would never leave. The old woman pushed a kitchen stool and a washtub into one of the bales. "You'll see," she said to her son. "We shall need all this in Moscow, and then I must keep something from sixty years of my life besides the ashes in my heart and the tears, which come even when I don't want to cry!" When they started sending her things to the station, the old woman's hollow cheeks again flushed over and her eyes shone with blind and passionate intensity. She scurried round the ransacked, dirty room, driven by some force that made her walk with her old and shaking shoulder touching the walls, from which the torn wallpaper hung down in strips.

The next morning—the day of their departure—Esther took her son and daughter to the cemetery. There, under Talmudic tombstones, in the gaps between ancient oak trees, were buried rabbis who had been killed by the Cos-

sacks of Honta and Khmelnitsky.[4] The old woman went
up to her husband's grave, shook slightly, and drew herself
up. "Marius," she said, "your son is taking me to Moscow.
Your son does not want me to be buried at your side. . . ."
She gazed steadily down at the reddish mound of crumbly,
porous earth, and her eyes grew wider and wider. Her son
and daughter held her by the arms. She swayed and
stumbled forward a little with her eyes half closed. She
tensed her wizened, sweating hands, surrendered to her
children, and then went limp. Her eyes grew still wider,
and were ablaze with light. She broke loose and flung
herself on the grave in her silk dress. Her whole body was
convulsed, and one of her hands stroked the red earth and
the withered flowers with hungry tenderness. Her shrill
voice echoed round the Jewish graveyard. "Your son is
taking me to Moscow, Marius. Pray for him to be happy
there, Marius. . . ." She passed her fingers, which were
crooked as though she were knitting, over the earth covering her dead husband. Then, when her son gave her his
hand, she quietly got up and went away with him. Boris
took her along a path overhung by the branches of oak
trees. His whole being was aching from the pressure of the
tears against the sockets of his eyes and in his throat. This
was his first taste of those tears that never go away and
remain inside a man forever. The old woman stopped by
the gate. She freed her hand, on which sweat welled up as
from an underground spring, alternately hot and ice cold,
and waved back at the cemetery and the grave, as though
they were floating away from her. "Goodbye, my dear,"
she said softly, no longer crying or shaking. "Goodbye! . . ."
   This was how the Erlichs left their native place.

IV

They traveled on the Sebastopol–Moscow express. Boris
had bought tickets for a "soft" car. They were driven to
the station by Boichik, the *balagula* who had once been
known all over town for his funny stories and his enormous
jet-black horses. But he no longer had these horses and his
ramshackle old carriage was now drawn by a huge white
nag with a drooping pink lip. Boichik himself was old
and rheumatic. "Listen, Boichik," said Esther, addressing
his round back as the carriage drew up to the station, "I
am coming back next year. I hope to find you well
then . . ." His back became even more hunched. The
white nag plodded through the mud on its stiff legs with
their swollen joints. Boichik turned round, showing his
red-rimmed eyelids, the twisted sash round his waist, and
the dirty tufts of hair growing out of his wizened little
face. "I doubt it, Madame Erlich . . ." And suddenly he
yelled at the horse: "Let's get back from the fair, come on
now . . ."

The "soft" car had been made out of several prewar
coaches. Through the broad, shining windows Esther
caught her last glimpse of her relatives huddled together
on the platform—the rust-colored raincoats, the soldiers'
leggings, the twisted capes, her old sisters with their large,
useless breasts, her brother-in-law Samuel, formerly a
commercial traveler, with his puffy, contorted face, her
other brother-in-law Efim, who had once been a very rich
man, with the rags wrapped around his old, withered, and
homeless legs. They jostled each other and shouted some-

thing as the train left. Her sister Genya ran along the platform. . . .[5]

Boris pointed out passing landmarks with such pride and
self-assurance, as though the whole country owed its existence and belonged to him, Boris Erlich. . . . Indeed, to
some extent this was even true: in everything they saw—
in the "international" coach they were traveling in, in the
newly built sugar-processing factories, in the reconstructed
railway stations—there was a drop of sweat or blood contributed by this corps commissar of the Red Cavalry . . .

In the evening he asked for bed linen for all three of
them, and with childlike pride he showed them how to
switch on the blue night light and, beaming all over his
face, revealed the secret of the little mahogany closet
which—presto!—could be converted into a washstand.

Lying between the large cool sheets, gently rocked by
the train's well-oiled springs, Esther stared out into the
blue darkness, from which all light had not yet faded, and
listening to the breathing of her son—he was shouting
and tossing in his sleep—and her daughter, she thought
how somebody would surely have to pay for this fairy
palace racing through Russia with its blazing lights and
shining brass tubes. This was a very Jewish thought. It
had not even occurred to Boris.

As they approached Moscow he was worried only about
whether Alyosha Selivanov had got his telegram asking
him to meet them at the station with a car. The car in
question was a new, thirty-thousand-ruble Packard for
the use of the general staff of the Red Army. It whisked
the Erlichs to an apartment, which had been prepared

well in advance by Boris, on the Ostozhenka. Alyosha had
even put some furniture in it already. Not giving his
mother time to recover from her joy at the infinite marvels
in the two rooms, Boris took her into the kitchen with its
gas range, the bathroom with its gas heater, and he
showed her the airing cupboards. The rooms were magnificent. They formed part of a suite which before the Revolution had belonged to the governor-general of Moscow.

As he ushered his mother through the kitchens, bath-
rooms, and mezzanine floor of this princely apartment,
Boris was unwittingly obeying the command of his ancient
Semitic blood. The cemetery and the grave of his luck-
less father, who had not lived to see all this, had aroused
in him that powerful family instinct which had sustained
his people for so many centuries. In his thirty-third year,
in response to this ancient call, he felt himself a father,
husband, and brother all in one: the defender of these
two women, their breadwinner and mainstay. He felt this
with all the intensity, with the painful and stubborn heart-
ache which come so easily to his people. He was tormented
by the thought that his father had not lived to see this,
and wanted to make up for this failure by seeing to it that
his father's wife and daughter came into good strong
hands. If their life in these new hands would be better than
it had been in his father's, this was only by virtue of the
implacable law of life.

v

Boris Erlich, a graduate of the Psycho-Neurological
Institute (because this was the only institute of higher
learning in pre-Revolutionary Russia which did not have

a *numerus clausus* for Jews), had spent the summer
vacations of 1917 with his parents in the *shtetl*. He had
gone round all the restive villages in the region and
explained to the peasants the fundamentals of Bolshevik
teaching. He was handicapped in his propaganda by his
curved nose, but only a little—the shape of your nose
didn't count for much in 1917. That same summer,
Alyosha, the son of the accountant to the local government board, returned from his Siberian exile in Ver-
khoyansk. While recovering from his imprisonment, and
consuming his parents' homemade cordials and cherry
dumplings, he did some research into his ancestry and
discovered that the Selivanovs were descended from
Selikha, a colonel of the Zaporozhyan Cossacks. In the
local archives he had even found a lithographed portrait
of his ancestor sitting on a horse in his Cossack greatcoat
and holding his mace of office. There was a faded inscrip-
tion in Latin under the portrait. Alyosha declared that it
was in the handwriting of Orlik, Mazeppa's Ukrainian
chancellor. Alyosha's romantic interest in the past was
combined with membership in the Socialist Revolutionary
Party.[6] The figures of Zhelyabov, Kibalchich, and Kalyayev[7] were constantly before his eyes. At the age of twenty-
one Alyosha led a very full life. His youthful fervor was
quickened by Boris Erlich, the hook-nosed graduate of the
institute with the funny name. They became close friends
and Alyosha joined the Bolsheviks when it became clear
that no other party in the world would have to fight,
destroy, and build as this party would have to, imbued as
it was with such mathematical and scholarly zeal. Boris
provided him with the necessary books and the *Communist Manifesto*. After the Revolution, Alyosha gathered

together all his friends in the *shtetl:* the nineteen-year-old Jewish projectionist from the Magic movie theater; the blacksmith, also Jewish; a few former N.C.O.'s who were kicking their heels with nothing to do; and some youths from the next village. He put them all on horseback and called the resulting detachment an "insurgent regiment of the Red Ukrainian Cossacks." One of the N.C.O.'s was made chief of staff and Boris was appointed commissar.

Since the men of Alyosha's regiment were fighting for a palpably just cause, got on well with each other, died with their heads held high, and lied like the devil, their ranks were constantly being swelled by new recruits, and the regiment developed in the same way as all the other rivulets which flowed together to make the Red Army. From a regiment it grew into a brigade, and from a brigade into a division; it fought against the Green Bands, Petlyura, Wrangel's Volunteer Army,[8] and the Poles. By the time of the campaign against Wrangel, Alyosha was already a corps commander. He was now twenty-four years old. Newspapers abroad wrote about Budyonny and Alyosha[9] as the inventors of new strategy and tactics for cavalry warfare. The specialists in the War Academy began to study his lightning cavalry raids, and the cadets in the Academy worked out exercises in tactics with reference to the operations of his Ukrainian Cossack Corps. Selivanov himself, and his inseparable commissar, Boris Erlich, who had been seconded to the Academy, also studied their own operations together with the cadets. In Moscow they set up a commune together with the former projectionist and the former N.C.O. of the Czarist army.

Just as in the corps, here too, in the Moscow commune, Boris held passionately, even morbidly, to the spirit of comradeship and the honor of the group. It was perhaps because his people had for so long been denied one of the finest of human feelings—that of comradeship in the field and in battle—that Boris felt such a hunger for friendship, a need to defend comrades and display loyalty to them. But despite its morbid side, there was so much that was attractive and fine in his passionate, chivalrous, and selfless approach to his comrades that Boris's apartment became a meeting place for the "Red marshals," as they were dubbed. This club really started to flourish when, instead of Moscow Cooperative Society sausage and vodka, gefilte fish began to appear on the table, the tin kettle was replaced by a samovar brought from Kremenets, and the tea was poured out by the comforting hand of an old woman. For many years Alyosha Selivanov and his brigade commanders had not seen an old woman sitting behind a samovar. It was a welcome change for them. The old woman was meek and timid, and as quiet as a mouse. But in her gelfilte fish and in her fingers, as they busied themselves with the samovar, one felt the essence of the Jewish people, its wholehearted and vehement passion.

VI

At first there was trouble over this fish. The professor's wife, who lived in the same building, said in the kitchen that the whole place stank to high heaven. And true enough—with the arrival of the Erlichs, even the entry hall began to smell of garlic and fried onion. [. . .]

Sulak

(1937)

"Sulak" (Sulak) *was first published in* The Young Kolkhoznik (Molodoi kolkhoznik), *No. 6, in 1937. Subsequently it appeared in* The Banner, *No. 8, in 1964 and it was included in both Soviet editions of Babel's* Collected Works *published in 1966.*

It is likely that Babel heard the story of Adrian Sulak during his trip to the Ukraine in the late twenties. The action takes place in 1928, just before the implementation of the first Five Year Plan. Like Babel's stories on collectivization ("Kolyvushka" and "Gapa Guzhva"), "Sulak" stresses the end of revolutionary anarchy and the consolidation of organized Soviet power.

Sulak

I N 1922, in the Vinnitsa region, the Gulay[1] band was
crushed. Gulay's chief of staff was Adrian Sulak, a
village schoolteacher. He managed to get abroad to Galicia
and before long there was a report in the newspapers
about his death. Six years after this we learned that Sulak
was alive and that he was hiding out in the Ukraine.
Chernyshev and I were instructed to find him. Armed
with papers saying we were veterinary surgeons, we set
off for Khoshchevatoye, the place where Sulak was born.
The chairman of the village soviet turned out to be a
demobilized Red Army man, a decent and straightforward
fellow.

"They'd grudge you a glass of milk in this place," he
told us. "They eat people alive in Khoshchevatoye . . ."

Inquiring about a place to stay the night, Chernyshev
brought the conversation round to Sulak's house.

"You could stay there," the chairman said. "The widow
has a room . . ."

He took us to the edge of the village, to a house with
a corrugated iron roof. In the upper room, in front of a
heap of linen, sat a tiny woman in a white loose-fitting
blouse. Two boys in orphanage dress, their shaven heads
bowed, were reading a book. A baby with a swollen,

bleached-looking head was asleep in a cradle. There was an air of cold, convent-like cleanliness about everything.

"Kharitina Terentyevna," the chairman said hesitantly, "I should like to put these good people up with you . . ."

The woman showed us the room and then returned to her linen.

"The widow can't refuse you," the chairman said as we left. "She's in a funny position . . ."

Glancing around him, he told us that Sulak had once served with the "yellow-and-blues"[2] and had now gone over to the Pope of Rome.

"Her husband's with the Pope of Rome," said Chernyshev, "but every year she brings a new child into the house."

"She does indeed," replied the chairman. He saw a horseshoe on the road and picked it up. "She may be undersized, but she can produce enough milk for five kids. The other women borrow milk from her . . ."

At home the chairman fried up some eggs and fat bacon and brought out a bottle of vodka. When he was drunk, he climbed up onto the tiled stove. We heard whispering and a child crying up there.

"Hanna baby, honest I will," our host was muttering, "honest I will—I'll go and see the teacher tomorrow . . ."

"Stop talking," shouted Chernyshev, who was lying next to me. "Let people sleep, will you . . ."

The disheveled chairman looked out from the top of the stove; his shirt was unbuttoned and his legs hung down.

"The teacher gave the kids some rabbits for breeding," he said apologetically. "She got a lady rabbit without a he . . . Come springtime it made off into the woods, of course."

"Hanna baby," the chairman suddenly said in a loud voice, speaking to the little girl. "I'll go and see teacher tomorrow, I'll bring you a pair and we'll make them a hutch . . ."

The father and his daughter went on talking for quite a time up on the stove and he kept on saying "Hanna baby." Then at last he went to sleep. Chernyshev tossed and turned on the hay next to me.

"Let's go," he said.

We got up. The moon was shining in a clear, cloudless sky. The puddles were lightly coated with spring ice. Sulak's garden, which was rank with weeds, bristled with cornstalks and was cluttered with scrap iron. In the stable next to the garden there was a rustling sound and a light glimmered in the cracks between the boards. Creeping up to the door, Chernyshev put his shoulder to it and the bolt gave. We went in and saw an open pit in the middle of the stable, and a man sitting at the bottom of it. The tiny woman in the white blouse was standing at the edge of the pit with a bowl of borscht in her hands.

"Hello, Adrian," Chernyshev said. "Just having your supper?"

Dropping the bowl, the tiny woman rushed at me and bit my hand. Her teeth were clenched tight, she shook and moaned. There was a shot from the pit.

"Adrian," Chernyshev said and jumped back, "we want you alive . . ."

Down below, Sulak struggled with the bolt of his gun; the bolt clicked.

"We're trying to talk to you like a human being," Chernyshev said and fired.

Sulak slumped against the yellow, smooth-planed wall; he groped at it with his hands, blood gushed from his mouth and ears, and he fell down.

Chernyshev stayed to keep watch while I went to fetch the chairman. We took the dead man away that same night. His boys walked alongside Chernyshev over the wet, softly gleaming road. The dead man's feet, in Polish boots with studs on the soles, peeped out of the wagon. The tiny woman sat stock-still at her husband's head. In the light of the darkening moon her face, with its contorted bones, looked as though it was made of metal. A child was asleep on her small knees.

"A good one for milk, is she?" Chernyshev said suddenly as he stalked on down the road. "I'll give her milk . . ."

Notes on the Stories

The Public Library

[1] This was the most luxurious food store on the Nevsky.

The Nine

[1] Leonid Nikolayevich Andreyev (1871–1919) and Yevdotia Apollonovna Nagrodskaya (1866–1939). His realistic stories and her novels advocating sexual freedom for women were extremely popular in Russia during the first decade of this century.

[2] Cadets stands for Constitutional Democratic Party.

Odessa

[1] Izya Kremer, born in Bessarabia in 1885, died in Argentina in 1956. She was a singer of Russian, Yiddish, and German ballads.

[2] Sergei Isayevich Utochkin (1874–1916). A native of Odessa and one of the aviation pioneers of Russia, he made a famous flight from Moscow to St. Petersburg in 1911.

[3] An extreme right-wing, anti-Semitic group responsible for pogroms.

[4] Babel here underlines the eclipse of Gogol's earlier vision as a writer of the sun (in his Ukrainian stories) by Petersburg gloom and introspection.

Akaki Akakiyevich is the pathetic anti-hero of Gogol's "The Overcoat" (1842).

Gritsko, a young and spirited peasant in Gogol's *Evenings on the Farm Near Dikanka* (1831–1832), wins a bride thanks to his charm and wits.

Taras Bulba, hero of Gogol's novel of the same name (1835); a ferocious Cossack captain.

Father Matvei Konstantinovsky was a fanatically ascetic priest under whose influence Gogol came during the last five years of his life. Matvei condemned his fictional writings as sinful and it is possible that this contributed to Gogol's decision to burn the second part of *Dead Souls*.

[5] The story referred to is "L'aveu," which figures prominently in Babel's story "Guy de Maupassant," published in 1932.

Mosaic

[1] Maria Fyodorovna was Princess Dagmar of Denmark and married Alexander III in 1866. The couple came to the throne in 1881; Czar Nicholas II was their son.

[2] Originally a place set aside in Russian towns for foreign merchants. Later the name was applied generally to any large row of shops.

[3] Ioann of Kronstadt (1829–1908), private confessor to Alexander III, was a St. Petersburg priest whose followers believed him capable of miracles and whose church at Kronstadt was an object of pilgrimage from all over Russia.

[4] A small city in the vicinity of St. Petersburg.

A Fine Institution

[1] Murman is another name for the Murmansk Coast. Murmansk is a port on the Barents Sea, on the Kola Peninsula; in 1917 the population numbered 3,000.

[2] Reference is made to the reforms which occurred during the reign (1855–1881) of Czar Alexander II. These reforms, the most important of which was the abolition of serfdom (1861), touched nearly every area of the political and social life of the Russian Empire.

The Blind Men

[1] Since 1914, Russia had suffered an almost unbroken sequence of military defeats which reached their peak in the autumn of 1917. The German armies seized Latvian and Estonian territories and occupied Riga on September 3, 1917. From that time on, Petrograd was under threat of German occupation.

Evacuees

[1] Major shipbuilding works.

[2] Sections of Petrograd with a large working-class population.

[3] See note for "The Blind Men" (above).

Premature Babies

[1] The Fontanka is a canal (the most famous of the many which run into the Neva) along which there are fancy ironwork railings.

[2] A fish closely related to the smelt and peculiar to the Neva.

The Palace of Motherhood

[1] Bartolomeo Francesco, Conte Rastrelli (1700–1771), was Russia's most famous and productive court architect. He built in the Italian baroque and rococo styles.

² Eminent aristocratic families which traced their genealogy back to the fifteenth century and which were always close to the Czars. The Stroganov Palace was reconstructed by Rastrelli.

³ Count Alexei Grigoryevich Razumovsky (1709–1771) was a favorite of the Empress Elizabeth, daughter of Peter the Great.

On the Field of Honor

¹ In the French text, the officer is narrator and the soldier is not identified. Vidal emphasizes the officer; Babel, the soldier.

² The French simply reads: "One of our guys squatting, shivering, with a wild look in his eyes." (*Un de nos types accroupi, frissonnant, les yeux égarés.*)

³ Probably a fictitious place name.

⁴ The humanization of the soldier and Babel's compassion for him are most evident in this brief obituary. Here is what Vidal wrote: "Then, goaded by this unbelievable outrage, he leapt forward, yelling, and began to run toward the enemy. Two minutes later, a bullet that went straight in the chest allowed one to say he had died a hero." (*Alors, sous l'outrage énorme, il bondit, hurlant, et se met à courir vers l'ennemi. Deux minutes après une balle en pleine poitrine permettait de dire qu'il était mort en héros.*)

The Deserter

¹ *C'est la défaite. Cela jamais* (That would be defeat! Never) is the only straightforward use of Vidal's text in this story. The other French colloquialisms are not found in Vidal.

² The soldier's name is Bridoux in Vidal's original.

An Evening at the Empress's

¹ See note 1 for "Mosaic."

[2] Anatoly Vasilyevich Lunacharsky (1875–1933) was the first People's Commissar for Enlightenment (i.e., cultural and educational matters).

[3] A common way of referring to Empress Alexandra (Alix of Hesse), wife of Nicholas II and daughter-in-law of the Dowager Empress Maria Fyodorovna, over whom she took precedence.

[4] Grand Duke Mikhail Alexandrovich (1878, executed 1918), son of Alexander III and Maria Fyodorovna, brother of Nicholas II.

A Hard-Working Woman

[1] An ordinary carriage with machine gun added. See Babel's Red Cavalry story, "Discourse on the *Tachanka*."

The Jewess

[1] A local military commander in Petlyura's army. See note 8.

[2] The People's Will (Narodnaya volya) was a revolutionary terrorist organization founded in 1879. It tried to achieve its aims by assassinating government officials. After killing Czar Alexander II, in March 1881, The People's Will itself fell victim to heightened police repression.

[3] Jean Jaurès (1859, assassinated 1914) and Jules Guesde (1845–1922) were French Socialist leaders.

[4] Bogdan Khmelnitsky, in the seventeenth century, and Ivan Honta, in the eighteenth, were Cossack leaders who rebelled against Polish rule and massacred Jews.

[5] In the original manuscript, a page is missing here.

[6] Founded in 1902, the SR Party was the successor to The People's Will (see note 2). In November 1917, after the Bolshevik coup, members of the Party were elected to fill the majority of seats in the Constituent Assembly. Lenin's government allowed the As-

sembly to meet only once before adjourning it sine die. The SR's, as a mass party, did not survive that event.

[7] Andrei Ivanovich Zhelyabov (1851–1881) was an influential member of The People's Will. He helped in the assassination of Alexander II and was himself executed a month later, on April 3, 1881.

Nicholas Ivanovich Kibalchich (1854–1881) was also a member of The People's Will. His specialty was homemade bombs.

Ivan Platonovich Kalyayev (1877–1905) was a member of The People's Will and a founder of the Socialist Revolutionary Party. On February 4, 1905, he threw the bomb which killed Grand Duke Sergei Alexandrovich, governor-general of Moscow. Kalyayev was hanged on May 10, 1905.

[8] The Green Bands were partisans who generally fought against both Whites and Reds during the Civil War.

Simon V. Petlyura (1879–1926), a leader of the Ukrainian Social Democratic Party who was prominent in several of the anti-Bolshevik regimes that rapidly replaced one another from 1917 to 1920. After the Red Army defeated the Poles, the fortunes of the Petlyurists fell and most of them escaped abroad. Petlyura himself went to Paris, where he was later assassinated.

Baron Peter Nikolayevich Wrangel (1878–1928), a Czarist general who led the White forces in South Russia in the final stages of the Civil War.

[9] Semyon M. Budyonny (1883–   ), marshal of the Soviet Union since 1935. During the Civil War he was, from November 1919 on, commander of the First Cavalry, to which Babel was attached as a correspondent.

The prototype for "Alyosha" was Alexei G. Selivanov, who had organized an uprising against the White commander-in-chief, Kaledin, during the early stages of the Civil War.

Sulak

[1] Gulay might refer to I. P. Gulay, organizer of a pro-Bolshevik partisan unit in the South of Russia in 1919. (It has not been possible to ascertain whether Sulak was a real person.)

[2] Ukrainian nationalists.

Appendices

Babel Answers Questions
about His Work

❁

The transcript of this rather ambiguous interview was not published until some twenty-seven years after it took place. Originally given before an audience at the Union of Soviet Writers on September 28, 1937, it appeared for the first time in the Moscow literary quarterly Our Contemporary *(Nash sovremennik), No. 4, in April 1964. The introductory note states that the interview "was the first of a series conceived and organized by the board of the Union of Soviet Writers and the editors of the magazine* Learning to Write *(Literaturnaya ucheba)," a monthly issued by the Union of Soviet Writers beginning in 1930.*

Babel began the evening's proceedings by reading aloud his recently published story "Di Grasso" and his story "Answer to an Inquiry," which had to wait until 1966 for publication in the Soviet Union. He then answered questions. His remarks, probably unrehearsed, were reproduced in Our Contemporary *"from an uncorrected shorthand transcript, with major cuts and essential editorial emendations." This text is translated here in its entirety.*

It is important to bear in mind the context of this interview. In 1937 Stalin's terror was in full swing and the slightest indiscretion could be fatal. But it was just as dangerous to refuse an interview as to give one. In trying to be both truthful and prudent, Babel was forced to steer a delicate course when touching on sensitive matters.

One such tricky subject was collectivization. During the first two years of collectivization, in 1929 and 1930, Babel had traveled extensively in the Ukraine and the Don Cossack country. He lived in villages and on collective farms; he wanted to take a close look at the transformations which the First Five-Year Plan had brought to a people renowned for their fierce independence.

In 1933 Babel again traveled to the Ukraine and then on to the Kabardino-Balkarian territory of the North Caucasus, from where he wrote to his family:

> *I am wandering across the Cossack steppes and am planning to settle in one place soon so that I can re-establish my lost contact with the world. I think if I take full advantage of this trip and do some serious work, it may produce major results . . . [Nalchik, November 8, 1933]**

> *I'm living in an old, pure-blooded Cossack settlement. The change-over to the collective farm system was not easy here and they have suffered hardships, but now it's all going ahead with a great deal of bustle. [Prishibskaya Cossack Settlement, December 13, 1933]†*

From such letters to relatives and friends we know that Babel had in mind, and was already working on, a loosely connected series of stories, each complete in itself but all dealing with the theme of collectivization in one Ukrainian village; namely, the village of Velikaya Staritsa, where Babel had lived in 1930. Only one of these stories, "Gapa Guzhva," had been published (in New World, *No. 1, 1931), under the subtitle "The First Chapter of* Velikaya Krinitsa," *when Babel gave this*

---

* *The Lonely Years,* p. 242.
† Ibid., p. 245.

interview. He had written to Vyacheslav Polonsky, the chief editor of the magazine, that he had purposely changed the name of the village.*

The story "Kolyvushka," first published in 1963 in New York, is the only other chapter of this cycle to survive. The tragic way in which it tells of a peasant dispossessed by the new order probably explains why Babel's other peasant stories never got into print.

We can see from all this one of the causes of Babel's celebrated "silence." But his limited output was nothing new. Babel's compulsion to rewrite, to produce endless variants—compounded by an increasing reluctance to part with his manuscripts until they met his own exacting standards—had plagued him since the beginning of his career. For example, we find him writing to Polonsky in January 1928:

> *For the third time I have started rewriting my stories and I find to my horror that still another revision is needed—the fourth. This will definitely be the last for the time being. [!] It can't be helped.†*

As we see from Georgy Munblit's reminiscences (see pages 259–273), Babel could be rather devious and had a large repertoire of tricks to play on his editors in order to gain time. Yet, in spite of this, Babel's silence was never absolute—indeed, he was at his most versatile in the thirties: "The Journey" appeared in March 1932, "Guy de Maupassant" in June 1932, "Oil" in February 1934, and "Dante Street" in March 1934. "Sulak" appeared in June 1937, followed by "The Kiss" in July and "Di Grasso" in August of the same year. Last to be published in his lifetime was the sketch "The Trial," in August 1938.

---

* Mentioned by E. Krasnoshchekova in *Star of the Orient,* No. 3, 1967, p. 109.

† Isaac Babel, *Collected Works* (Moscow, 1966), p. 442.

Babel not only continued to write throughout the thirties but, as is clear from his correspondence, he even experimented with new forms. Furthermore, he now had the urge to write longer works, as we see from his mention of a plan for "a novel of about 300 pages."* "The Jewess," probably a fragment of this intended novel, is, though unfinished, his longest known work of prose fiction.

In the mid-thirties, Babel turned away from prose and spent many months working on plays and film scripts.† As far as we know, however, only one of these dramatic works has survived, the play Maria.

But, as indicated above, Babel's "silence" was just as much due to the difficulties that he encountered in getting into print material he was ready to publish. In 1933 Gorky recommended four of his stories for publication in the miscellany The Sixteenth Year *(God shestnadtsaty): "Froim Grach," "My First Fee," "Oil," and "Dante Street." All of them were turned down in spite of Gorky's patronage. Only "Oil" and "Dante Street" were published in 1934 in other magazines. ("Froim Grach" and "My First Fee" were published first in New York in 1963 and only very recently in the Soviet Union.) Publication of a "collectivization" story, "Adrian Morinets," was announced in* New World *but it never appeared. Babel's play* Maria, *published in March 1935, drew such harsh official criticism that rehearsals were stopped at the Vakhtangov Theatre in Moscow. It was not until 1964 that* Maria *was at last staged—by the Piccolo Theatre in Italy.*

In the light of all these difficulties, one must admire the skill with which Babel handled the questions thrown at him, during

---

* In a letter to Polonsky dated April 1929, published in *The Banner,* No. 8, 1964, p. 159.

† As evidenced by Babel's letters to his family in 1935. See *The Lonely Years,* pp. 272, 275, 279.

*the interview, about his "puzzling" lack of productivity. He
accepted the reproaches, with the somewhat startling explana-
tion: "I am simply not very well equipped to do this job, and I
wouldn't do it if I felt in a better position to do something else."
Then, in the next breath, he found a way of confusing the entire
issue:*

> *By temperament I am always interested in the how and the why.
> These questions need careful thought and study, and you have to
> approach the business of writing with great honesty in order to
> answer them in literary form. That's how I explain it [my silence]
> to myself.*

*Almost all of Babel's answers are marked by a similar am-
biguity. What he did not say is as significant as what he said.
Only caution could have induced him, for example, to omit
the names of Leskov, Gogol, and Dostoevsky as his "favorite
writers." He no doubt believed that Tolstoy is "the most
marvelous writer who ever lived," but of all his works Babel
singles out "Hadji-Murad," a late story of a Caucasian mountaineer chief who, in the words of D. S. Mirsky, has "all
the virtues and all the vices of a warlike barbarian." This
definition applies equally well to Babel's Cossacks.*

*Then, what is one to make of the moderate praise bestowed
on Sholokhov ("[He] is progressing along the right lines")
when it is followed a little later by such a bitterly ironical
remark as:*

> *Now, to forestall the slightest suggestion that I am running myself
> down, I should add that many of my comrades, even though
> their store of interesting facts and observations is no larger than
> mine, nevertheless write them up in "Tolstoyan" fashion. What
> this leads to is known to all their victims.*

*The interview might be read as a masterpiece of double-
entendre, but this is not the main impression it leaves. On the*

surface, the tone may be jocose and sanguine, but underneath there is frustration, bitterness, and painful ambivalence; what we see is an almost desperate affirmation of an individuality that was plainly too much for the Soviet authorities in 1937. No wonder the interview was not published at the time.

Q: *Are you writing less about the Civil War now?*
B: I should say that after a fairly long period of wandering around in circles I am now finding it easier to write. I am writing quite a lot, and it will be published. I now look at the Civil War in a different way.

I have new themes. I want to write about the countryside, about collectivization (that interests me very much at the moment), about people during collectivization, about the transformation of agriculture. This is the greatest event of our Revolution, apart from the Civil War. I was more or less closely involved in collectivization in 1929–1930 and for a few years now I've been trying to describe it. It looks as though I am now succeeding.

Q: *How long did it take you to write your first story?*
B: Since this evening was arranged by the magazine *Learning to Write*, I think questions about working methods are appropriate. And this is what I can say about myself.

When I first began to write short stories, my "technique" was to think for a long time beforehand, so that when I sat down to write I almost knew the story by heart—it was so "ripe" that it just went straight onto paper. I could go for three months and then write half a page in three or four hours, almost without any crossing out.

Later I became disillusioned with this method—I found that everything was cut and dried before the actual writing, and there was little scope for improvisation. When you put pen to paper, there's no telling where it may lead you or where the devil you may end up. You don't always fall in with the rhythm or with the expressions as they've taken shape in your mind.

Now I work differently. Whenever I get the urge to write something—say, a story—I just write as the mood strikes me. Then I put it aside for a few months, after which I go through it again and rewrite it. I can rewrite something any number of times—in this respect, I have great patience. I think that this method—as you can see from the stories that are going to be published*—leads to greater facility, greater fluency in the telling of the story, and greater directness.

Q: *Readers are puzzled by your more than lengthy silence.*
B: It puzzles me too, so in this respect there's not much difference between us.

To tell the honest truth, I am simply not very well equipped to do this job, and I wouldn't do it if I felt in a better position to do something else. But this is the only job that, with a great deal of effort, I can do more or less decently. That's the first thing. In the second place, I have a well-developed critical sense. In the third place, we live in stormy, revolutionary times and I am among those people who are not so concerned with the word "what." I am quick to feel admiration, hatred, or sorrow. Some comrades, when they feel these things, immediately rush to put it down on paper, and if they are accomplished journalists, or if they are good at writing odes or satires, then it sometimes turns out very well. By temperament I am always interested in the how and the why. These questions need careful thought and study, and you have to approach the

---

* Only one more of Babel's stories was to be published before his arrest in May 1939. Entitled "The Trial" (*Sud*) and not dated, it appeared in the weekly *The Flame* (*Ogonyok*) on August 20, 1938. It has been included in the various editions of his *Collected Works* published in the Soviet Union since 1957. An English translation by Andrew R. MacAndrew appears in *Lyubka the Cossack and Other Stories*.

This "trial" of an émigré taxi driver in Paris is noteworthy mainly for its brevity and its irrelevance to the Soviet scene. It is by no means one of Babel's best or most characteristic efforts, and it certainly does not demonstrate any "new method" of writing.

business of writing with great honesty in order to answer them in literary form. That's how I explain it [my silence] to myself.

Furthermore, I'm an old offender in this respect. It's nothing new for me. I started writing as a youth, then gave it up for a number of years, then wrote like fury for a few years, then stopped again, and now I'm beginning the second act of the comedy, or tragedy—I don't know what it will be. In general it's biography [autobiography?], but rather awkward biography.

Q: *Please tell us who your favorite authors, classical and modern, are and whom you have learned from.*

B: Recently I've been concentrating more and more on one writer—Leo Nikolayevich Tolstoy. Pushkin, I need hardly say, is a constant companion. I think that our budding writers do not spend enough time reading and studying Tolstoy—surely the most marvelous writer who ever lived.

I must say that when I reread *Hadji-Murad*° a few years ago, I was shaken quite beyond description. I remember what Gorky once said to me. Everybody knows Gorky's *Recollections of Tolstoy,* but it is not generally known that Gorky also worked for many years of his life on a book about Tolstoy, which, he told me, he just couldn't get done. I think the reason is that the first book was written under the immediate impact, with passion, while in the second he was trying to write a treatise . . .

As I read *Hadji-Murad* again, I thought: this is the man one should learn from. Here the electric charge went from the earth, through the hands, straight to the paper, with no insulation at all, quite mercilessly stripping off all outer layers with a sense of truth—a truth, furthermore, which was clothed in dress both transparent and beautiful.

° *Hadji-Murad,* begun in 1896 and completed in 1904, was first published in 1911, in the posthumous edition of Tolstoy's collected works. See note on page 217.

When you read Tolstoy, you feel that the world is writing, the world in all its variety. In fact, people say, it's all a matter of devices, of technique. If you take any chapter of Tolstoy's, you will find great heaps of everything—there is philosophy, death. And you might think that to write like this you need legerdemain, extraordinary technical skill. But all this is submerged in the feeling for the universe by which Tolstoy was guided.

As a literary critic I'm not only no good, I'm terrible. I must apologize for talking this kind of stuff. But I'm trying to answer the question about my favorite classical writers and whom one should learn from.

As to modern writers, I think we are approaching a time of "the Hamburg reckoning," to borrow the term once used by Shklovsky.° Personally, I don't believe that a writer is someone with a kind of physical aptitude for writing, that he has something pressing on his brain that pushes his pen, that his heart and mind are more highly developed than other people's. I think we are nearing a time when scholastic, artificial works, works not imbued with feeling and sincerity, will be on their way out, and will no longer clutter up our literature.

If I'm to mention any names, then I think Sholokhov† is progressing along the right lines. Here is somebody whose writing has a good texture. When you read him, you *see* what is written, and it's done with passion. The fabric of his work is not as significant as it is in Tolstoy; when Tolstoy has a

---

° Viktor Borisovich Shklovsky (1893–   ), writer and leading Formalist theoretician. In the thirties he renounced Formalism, when it became anathema to the advocates of Socialist Realism. The title of his book *The Hamburg Reckoning* (*Gamburgsky shchët,* 1928) refers to a system of assessing the form and thereby the quality of prize fighters. Shklovsky, like Babel, applied the term to writers.

† Mikhail Alexandrovich Sholokhov (1905–   ), leading Soviet writer whose four-volume epic novel *And Quiet Flows the Don* (1928–1940) brought him international fame. He received the Nobel Prize for Literature in 1965. *Virgin Soil Upturned,* a novel about collectivization, was published in 1931. It is considered one of the classics of Socialist Realism.

gentleman come out of a house and say, "Cabbie, twenty-five kopecks to Tverskaya," it has the ring of a world event in harmony with the universal order of things.

There can be no question of details having such significance in Sholokhov, but I think he has a lot in him and he's on the right path.

I have a very high opinion of Valentin Katayev,* who, I think, will be writing better and better, who has already evolved in a very sound way, who becomes more serious as he gets older, and whose *Lonely White Sail* I regard as an out-standingly useful contribution to Soviet literature. This book of Katayev's has done a great deal to bring Soviet literature back to the grand tradition of three-dimensional writing, of simplicity, of descriptive art, which we have all but lost. We have almost no one who knows how to *show* a thing. Instead, they talk about it very longwindedly, and this way of writing is terrible. In my opinion, Valentin Katayev is very much an up-and-coming writer and his work will get better all the time. He is one of our great hopes.

Q: *From what you've been saying, one might think that you are a great believer in things being on a large scale and well made, that you believe in realism, and that you take your cue from Tolstoy and Sholokhov. How does this square with what we find in your own work? Your work might make one think that what interests you most in life is the exceptional, rather than the typical. Yet, realism is the cornerstone of your artistic philosophy.*

B: In one of Goethe's letters to Eckermann, I came across a definition of the novella, the short story—the form in which I feel more at home than in any other. Goethe's definition of the novella was very simple: it is a story about an unusual occur-

---

* Born in Odessa in 1897, Valentin Petrovich Katayev started his literary career in the twenties, with stories of an experimental nature. His best-known novels are *The Embezzlers* (1926), *Time, Forward!* (1932), *Lonely White Sail* (1936), and *The Holy Well* (1966).

rence. Perhaps this is wrong—I don't know—but that's what Goethe thought.

I don't think I have the powers, the equipment, or the urge to record the typical as voluminously as Tolstoy did. I like to read him, but I have no interest in trying to write in his manner.

You talk about my silence. Let me tell you a secret. I have wasted several years trying, with due regard to my own tastes, to write lengthily, with a lot of detail and philosophy—striving for the sort of truth I have been talking about. It didn't work out with me. And so, although I'm a devotee of Tolstoy, in order to achieve something I have to work in a way opposite to his.

I understand your question very well, but I seem to have answered it very unclearly. Let me put it this way: the point is that Tolstoy was able to describe what happened to him minute by minute, he remembered it all, whereas I, evidently, only have it in me to describe the most interesting five minutes I've experienced in twenty-four hours. Hence the short-story form. That must be the reason.

Q: *So Tolstoy ran to 23 hours 55 minutes more than you?*

B: Well now, self-deprecation is just not in my nature. And if I wanted to make my life a misery by wondering who writes better, Tolstoy or I—even supposing I came to the conclusion that he wrote better, I would probably loathe and detest him.

But since we are here under the auspices of *Learning to Write*, and can talk about trade secrets, I have told you why I can more or less manage short things but not long ones. Now, to forestall the slightest suggestion that I am running myself down, I should add that many of my comrades, even though their store of interesting facts and observations is no larger than mine, nevertheless write them up in "Tolstoyan" fashion. What this leads to is known to all their victims.

Q: *In your very well written stories there are one or two phrases which seem to me on the audacious side. In one story you have the words "kind legs." I don't see how legs can be either kind or cruel. In another story you have the sentence: "He shook his head like a startled bird." If a bird is frightened, it flies away.*

B: As for the first story, that phrase jarred you because it didn't carry conviction, but human legs can be good, cruel, seeing, or blind. There's no doubt that legs can have any of these human attributes—one just has to be able to describe it. That story ends a little abruptly, and the point doesn't come through. You're right about that.

As to the other phrase—to me it just seems plausible. That's how I feel about it. On the point about audacity—this, as we know, is a virtue, but only if a man rushes into battle bearing the right weapons. In this sense audacity is a good thing.

I think it would be good to talk a little about the technique of short-story writing, because the form is not very popular with us. It must be said that it has never really caught on in this country—the French have always been ahead of us there. Actually, our only real short-story writer is Chekhov. Most of Gorky's short stories are condensed novels. Tolstoy's short stories are also condensed novels—except for "After the Ball,"* which is a real short story. On the whole, we don't do very well with short stories—we go in much more for novels.

Q: *What is your opinion of Paustovsky?†*

B: Highly favorable. If I had gone on with what I was saying

---

* This "real short story," dated August 1903, is nine pages long. Like *Hadji-Murad* (see note on page 213), it is one of Tolstoy's last works.

† Konstantin Georgiyevich Paustovsky (1892–1968), Soviet man of letters. His celebrated memoirs have been published in English in two volumes: *The Story of a Life* (New York: Pantheon Books, 1964) and *Years of Hope* (New York: Pantheon Books, 1969), the second of which deals at length with Babel. For more Paustovsky reminiscences of Babel, see page 275.

about Sholokhov and Katayev, I should also have had to mention Paustovsky and his interesting development as a writer. I have known him for a long time—we come from the same place. I read his first attempts at writing. They are a very good illustration of what I was saying about [my?] first story. Those first attempts of Paustovsky's were so longwinded, confused, and ineptly written—although he was a grown man by then. He wasn't eighteen or twenty, he was twenty-five, twenty-six, or twenty-seven. It was all so overloaded with adjectives and metaphors, it was so lush that the reader was literally overwhelmed—in the heady atmosphere he created, it was difficult to breathe. It was a conservatory of tropical flowers in a badly constructed hothouse. But, with all this, you could always see genuine feeling. Then, for fifteen years, Paustovsky worked at refining this feeling, at getting rid of much of the dross. And now we see the result—what is interesting is what he has started to write at the age of forty.

Q: *Tolstoy never had to work like that.*

B: That's more bad news for us all. Actually, Tolstoy ended just as he began. He found the form and substance of what he had to say right at the start—it just became terser and terser as time went on. When he was seventy-five or eighty-two he set down what he had to say in a physical rather than a literary form, in a way that conveyed every shade of meaning.

Q: *You believe in short sentences. What do you think: should an idea be spun out or only hinted at, in a short story?*

B: That's a terrible misapprehension. I don't believe in short sentences. I believe in alternating short sentences and long ones, also that human thought needs punctuation marks. That's all.

Now, as to whether ideas should be spun out or only hinted at: they should be put precisely, comrade. One would like to see ideas conveyed intact, not "spun out."

Q: *Do you think that Yuri Olesha* has written himself out, or will he go on writing? What do you think of him?*

B: You keep asking questions which apply to me as well, and about people extremely close to me. We are all from the same part of the country—and belong to the so-called Odessa or "South Russian" school, of which I think very highly. I have a very high opinion of Yuri Olesha. I regard him as one of the most talented and original of Soviet writers. Will he go on writing? There is nothing else he can do. If he goes on living, he will go on writing. I think he can write magnificently; I think his ability to produce is blocked by imaginary obstacles. His talent will crash through this barrier. Olesha is a major writer.

Q: *Isn't he a little too keen on journalism? Perhaps this prevents him from working.*

B: Yuri Karlovich Olesha is a public speaker by his very nature. He can speak about abstract matters or about topical ones. I don't see any hard and fast division between his articles and his other work. The articles are written rather hastily, they're less significant, but there is always some mark of originality in them.

---

* Yuri Karlovich Olesha (1899–1960), whose most famous work is *Envy* (1927), disappeared from the Soviet literary scene in 1938. His rehabilitation during the Thaw was signaled by the publication of a one-volume edition of *Selected Works* in Moscow in 1956.

The boldness of Babel's response to the interviewer can be appreciated only in the light of the severe attacks from Soviet critics to which Olesha had been subjected in the thirties. Olesha made a speech at the First Congress of the Union of Soviet Writers in Moscow, August 1934, in which, to quote Gleb Struve, "He had the courage to say that every artist could create only within his powers: 'A writer can write only what he can write.' He candidly admitted that it was impossible for him to put himself into the shoes of an average workman or of a revolutionary hero, and therefore he could not write about either of them." (Gleb Struve, *Soviet Russian Literature* [London: Routledge & Sons, 1935], p. 236.)

Olesha's difficulty in adjusting to the subordination of literature to Soviet policy led him to publish less and less. Babel's sentence "If he goes on living, he will go on writing" might be an allusion to Olesha's heavy drinking, as well as to the menacing atmosphere of the time.

Q: *What's the way to work on a novella?*

B: How to work on a short story? I have absolutely no faith in recipes or textbooks and, by the way—I'm ashamed to say it, and perhaps it's a reactionary viewpoint, but I'm very alarmed by the [Gorky] Literary Institute.* I realize that what they're doing there is raising the level of people's education and qualifications. That is very important—if they teach people French and English, all well and good, but how can you teach a person to *write?* This I don't understand. Here I can only speak of my own personal experience.

I try to choose my readers, and, in so doing, I try not to set my sights too low. I aim at a reader who is intelligent, educated, and has good, exacting taste. Generally speaking, I feel that a short story can be read properly only by a very intelligent woman—the better specimens of this half of the human race sometimes have absolute taste, just as some people have absolute pitch. The most important thing here is to form a picture of one's reader—a picture as strict as possible. That's how it is with me. My reader lives in my soul, but since he's been there quite a long time, I have fashioned him in my own image. Perhaps he's even become one with me.

After you've written a story, you must never, in a state of wild excitement, read it to someone else; don't rush to break the great news that you've given birth. This is not so easy. It takes a lot of effort to keep from rushing next door and reading it, to let it lie for a while and then take a fresh look at it. . . . Just as I choose my reader, I also think how I can best get around this clever fellow, or bowl him over. I respect him. The old actor's idea that "the public are fools" is a terrible thing. You must aim at some serious critic or other and try to

---

* The Gorky Literary Institute was established in Moscow in 1933 for the purpose of educating and developing young Soviet writers in the Communist spirit.

knock him unconscious. That's the sort of ambition you must have. Once this ambition is aroused, you have no time for tom-foolery.

My attitude toward adjectives is the story of my life. If ever I write my autobiography, I'll call it *The Story of an Adjective.* In my youth I thought that the sumptuous must be conveyed by sumptuous means. But I was wrong. It turned out that one must very often proceed by opposites . . . All my life I have nearly always known *what* to write, but since I tried to get it all on twelve pages, since I have restricted myself in this way, I have had to pick and choose words that are, first, significant; second, simple; and third, beautiful.

Q: *Why aren't you more satisfied with the things you've written?*

B: I think the things I have written could have been better and simpler. But I was one of those people who in their youth accept even pimples as natural. Perhaps I'm wrong, perhaps I'm blinded by conceit, but I think I see what I want to say and how to say it better now than I did then, when I wrote those things. The only cause I have for satisfaction is that I don't have to take back anything I've written.

The Moscow Commemoration of
Babel's Seventieth Birthday

On November 11, 1964, an evening of speeches and readings honoring Babel's seventieth birthday was held in the headquarters of the Union of Soviet Writers in Moscow; the fact that permission for this had been granted was an accomplishment in itself. The celebration attracted an enormous audience —old and young—many of whom had to remain in the street for lack of seats. Loudspeakers were hastily installed for them.

The evening was memorable in many ways. Presided over by Konstantin Alexandrovich Fedin (1892–), the Secretary General of the Union of Soviet Writers, it gave the official stamp that was needed to sanction the reacceptance of Babel by the Soviet literary establishment. Most of the participants— the writers who made speeches and the actors who read some of Babel's stories—were Babel's contemporaries, and some had been his friends. They were of the generation that had undergone the hardships not only of the revolutionary years but of Stalinism at its worst; unlike the postwar generation, they had not lost the habit of fearing any encounter with officialdom. Whether from a philosophical strength that had come with age or from a feeling that public justice must be done, on this occasion they came forward and spoke up in homage to a man whose work had long been considered subversive.

Among the participants was the poet Vera Inber (1890–   ), who might have recalled that some thirty years earlier, in 1935, she, Babel, Olesha, and Paustovsky, all representatives of the so-called Odessa school, had made speeches on the first anniversary of the death of their fellow Odessan, the poet Eduard Bagritsky. The writer Lev Nikulin (1891–1967), who had gone through all the proper motions during the various phases of Stalinism, was there too.

Ilya Ehrenburg (1891–1967), who had been influential in the planning of the anniversary celebration, closed the evening, well after midnight. By that time he had reached the high emotional pitch that his speech reflects. It is published here for the first time in any language, translated from a shorthand transcript that was made as he spoke.

The Moscow celebration of Babel's seventieth birthday was the result of persistent efforts. Step by step, the groundwork for this moment had been laid during the previous spring and summer, as the seven-year silence that followed the "rehabilitation" edition of 1957 was broken. In April 1964 the hitherto unpublished transcript of a 1937 interview with Babel appeared (see page 205). So did Livshits's critical essay "Material for a Literary Biography of I. Babel."* Here Livshits quotes the diary Babel kept during the 1920 Polish campaign, which until then only Ehrenburg was known to have seen. Livshits also acknowledges his use of the edition of Babel's correspondence that had been published in Italy in 1961. Although he makes no mention of The Lonely Years, the American edition of stories and letters, it certainly had not gone unnoticed. On the contrary, the book may well have provided Soviet scholars with a lever for lifting the censorship that Soviet officials had continued to impose on Babel. Indeed, shortly after publication of The Lonely Years, in August 1964, some fifty pages of issue

---

* L. Livshits, op. cit., pp. 110–135.

No. 8 of the literary magazine The Banner were devoted to Babel. Of the eight Babel stories which appeared in that issue, four are in The Lonely Years ("Ilya Isaakovich and Margarita Prokofyevna," "Mamma, Rimma and Alla," "Gapa Guzhva," and "Froim Grach"). Some fifty long excerpts from Babel's "Letters to Friends" were also published, for the first time in the Soviet Union. The final item in this Babel section was Georgy Munblit's "Reminiscences of Babel" (see page 259). And in July of the same year, Lev Nikulin had published his pointed if belated admission that he had known and admired Babel (see page 239). Prepared in this way, and thrown open to the public, the celebration had an impact all the more forceful.

If Ilya Ehrenburg felt he owed a debt to Babel, he partially paid it on this occasion. His bold manner of expression and vehement demands that Babel's works be reissued may have accounted for some of the publications that soon followed. Such pleas from a quasi-official platform were, it seems, the signal needed to open old files and spark new editions. A week after the celebration, Livshits published the story "Sunset" (see page 135). 1965 saw the publication of Volume 74 in the series Literary Heritage, with a section on Babel containing extensive critical studies of his known and unknown writings by his most thorough and honest critic, the Soviet scholar I. A. Smirin;* rather extensive quotations from Babel's diary; and the story "You Must Know Everything" (see page 1). Konstantin Paustovsky's moving tribute appeared in a Moscow newspaper in September 1966 (see page 275). And in the winter of 1966 the long-awaited new edition of Babel's Collected Works, with a preface by Ehrenburg and notes by Munblit, was published in Kemerovo, a coal-mining town 2,000 miles

---

* In 1961 I. A. Smirin defended a doctoral dissertation on Babel at the University of Alma-Ata.

east of Moscow; it includes "Answer to an Inquiry," another of the stories published in The Lonely Years. *This volume was speedily followed by a Moscow edition, introduced by L. Polyak and edited by E. Krasnoshchekova, which is the fullest selection of Babel's stories ever to appear in book form in the Soviet Union. It also contains his two plays; numerous letters to literary personalities; and a group of miscellaneous pieces, including the speech given by Babel at the Congress of Soviet Writers in Moscow in 1934, which had been published, for the first time since that year, in* The Lonely Years.

Another extraordinary publication followed in the spring of 1967. Star of the Orient, *the monthly journal of the Union of Writers of Uzbekistan, devoted its March issue to an anthology of Soviet writing, mostly of outstanding quality. The section devoted to Babel offers two "forgotten" stories, "Bagrat-Ogly and the Eyes of His Bull" (see page 111) and "Grishchuk" (see page 119); and two stories never before published in the Soviet Union, "My First Fee" and "Kolyvushka," both of which had appeared in* The Lonely Years. *In an introductory note, E. Krasnoshchekova quotes Babel's "letters to relatives" (i.e., letters from* The Lonely Years) *and defends her choice of these rather unorthodox stories. One may surmise that the four stories had not been considered acceptable for the Moscow edition of* Collected Works, *also edited by Madame Krasnoshchekova. Now they had found their way to Tashkent, much further from the censors' eyes.*

Most recently, a very informative chapter on Babel by L. Polyak, a specialist in Soviet literature at Moscow University, has been added to the first volume of the "corrected and enlarged" second edition of the History of Russian Soviet Literature (Istoria russkoi Sovetskoi literatury), *published in Moscow in 1967. The first edition, dated 1958–1963, made only cursory references to* Red Cavalry *and disposed of the rest of Babel's work in four lines.*

Ehrenburg's speech is followed here by the three memoirs referred to above. Written by men of various literary stature and political inclination, these stand as tributes to Babel the man and the writer. They show a genuine effort on the part of men of his own generation to restore him to a literature from which his very name was banished and to a country for which he gave his life.

ILYA EHRENBURG

A Speech at a Moscow Meeting
in Honor of Babel, November 11, 1964*

❁

I HAD to come here and speak today even though many others
have talked so well about Isaac Emmanuelovich and even
though I have written about him.†

He was the greatest friend I have ever had. He was three
and a half years younger than I, but I used to call him, jokingly,
"the wise old rabbi," because he was a wise man. He wasn't
a clever man, or a learned man; he was a wise man. He had
an extraordinary ability to see life in depth. He understood
that the human eye cannot take in the infinite, and he took a
rather poor view of writers—however distinguished they were
and however much he liked them personally—who tried to see
everything.

He was always saying: "It should be a little deeper." He
only wanted to see what he could see deeply.

When people say he was a romantic, they are talking the

---

* This transcript is a rather rough one; there are a few obscure passages
and it is probably incomplete. Words and phrases in brackets have been
added by the translator to clarify the sense of the original.

† Ehrenburg had written the introduction to the 1957 Soviet edition
of Babel's *Collected Works* and was to write another for one of the two
1966 editions. In his *Memoirs: 1921–41* (New York: The World Publishing Company, 1964), he often mentions his encounters with Babel and
reminisces about him.

language of literary historians or schoolgirls. It's true that he liked to play the fool and put on romantic airs. He liked to create an atmosphere of mystery about himself; he was very secretive and never told anybody where he was going.

In Paris once he set out to come to see me, but he never arrived. It turned out that his daughter had asked him, "Where are you going?" He couldn't bring himself to lie to her and said, "To Ehrenburg." But once he had said this, he couldn't come to see me, and he walked off in the opposite direction.

Writing was sheer agony for him, and he would rewrite the same page dozens of times. It often took him a day to do a quarter of a page, and even at the best of times he could only manage half a page.

In Paris he took lodgings in the house of a mad Frenchwoman. She was frightened of him, thought he was a bandit, and said she would have him locked up. He lived a long way out, in a suburb of Paris.

Babel never had much money, and although he knew how to talk with publishers, he never got much out of them. When he was a young man, he took good care of his mother, his sister, his first wife and their daughter, and then, in his later years, of his second family in Moscow.* He sent his mother money, but in a devious way, speaking mysteriously in his letters, which have now been published,† about sending books: "The first volume will be small—only fifty pages." This meant that he had managed to get fifty francs to her.

He was not a romantic in art. The term "realism" is com-

---

* When it became apparent, after 1935, that Babel would not be permitted to leave the Soviet Union again, he wed by common law Antonina Nikolayevna Pirozhkova. Their daughter Lidya, my half sister, was born in January 1937. She and her mother live in Moscow.

† Babel's correspondence with his mother and sister, who had emigrated to Belgium, has indeed been published, in Milan in 1961 (*Racconti proibiti e lettere intime*), in New York in 1964 (*The Lonely Years, 1925–1939*), and in Paris (*Correspondance, 1925–1939*, Gallimard, 1967); but not in Moscow.

pletely applicable to him, but it was a *human* realism—this is the only adjective one can use with the word in his case.

How did he mitigate the cruelty you can find in nearly all his stories? By love, by a conspiracy of compassion with his heroes and readers, by his enormous kindness of heart. He was a very kind man and a good man, not in the commonplace sense of the expression but in a very real sense, and what people say about his not having believed in the success of writers who were lukewarm in spirit sums up very well the whole nature of Isaac Emmanuelovich.

While waiting for me once in my apartment in Paris, he reread a short story by Chekhov, and when I came—I was late —he said, "You know, it's extraordinary: Chekhov was a very kind man."

What people have said about [his attitude to] Maupassant— this is really about the shattering effect of the brilliance of Maupassant's short stories on a Russian writer used to the sort of literature published in the *Znanye* annuals.*

He quarreled with any Frenchman who dared to find the slightest fault with Maupassant and maintained that he was flawless, but in one of the last conversations I had with him, he said, "Everything about Maupassant was fine, but he was lacking in heart." He had suddenly come to feel Maupassant's streak of terrible loneliness and withdrawnness.

Babel had an enormous curiosity. I cannot say that the Babel I knew was a cheerful person; he had none of the cheerfulness, false optimism, or other things needed to win approval.

He was a sad person who was able to laugh and who had had a very interesting life.

In life he was particularly interested in the two mysteries

---

* *Znanye* (*Knowledge*), a publishing firm founded in St. Petersburg in 1898 whose chief editor from 1900 to 1919 was Maxim Gorky. Its literary annual featured both Russian and foreign literature, with emphasis on writers of peasant and proletarian background.

that interest everybody, whatever their age: love and death. I can well believe the story that in Odessa he used to treat people to something in return for the story of their first love. The number of confidences he must have heard! He was very good at getting them out of people. In Paris, where he was always short of money, he was quite capable of paying a girl whatever she asked, and going without dinner, to sit and talk with her in a café. He could not see a lady's handbag without asking, often to no avail: "Can I see what you've got in there?"

I remember those days very well. Babel could be very cautious. It cannot be said that he was the sort of person who rushed into things blind. He knew that he should not have frequented the house of Yezhov,* but he wanted to fathom the riddle of man's life and death.

At one of our last meetings—it was at the time when they were at last letting me out to go to Spain†—we sat in the restaurant of the Metropole Hotel. There was dancing and the band was playing, and, leaning over to me, he said in a whisper, "Yezhov is only the instrument." This was after lengthy visits to Yezhov's house and conversations with Yezhov's wife, whom he had known for a long time. This is the only piece of good sense I remember hearing during the whole of that time. Babel saw and understood what was going on better than any of us. Here was a man, if ever there was one, who never thought in abstractions, but always in terms of living people.

He was formed by the Revolution, and the fate of the man we see here before us (*pointing to portrait*) was tragic. He was one of the writers most devoted to the Revolution, and he

---

* Nikolai Ivanovich Yezhov (1895–1938?) was the head of the Secret Police (NKVD) during the two years of purges and terror (1936–1938) which went by the name of Yezhovshchina. Stalin replaced him with Beria in 1938, and Yezhov subsequently was executed.
† Ehrenburg was a correspondent during the Spanish Civil War.

believed in progress. He believed that everything would turn out for the best.

Whenever he wrote a story and was putting the finishing touches to it, he thought not of publication but [of how best to express] his deep conviction.

And then they killed him.

I remember once when he came to see me in Lavrushinsky Street, in a very gloomy mood, at the beginning of 1938. He sat down, looked around, and said, "Let's go into the other room." He was afraid to talk in the room where the telephone was.*

We went into the other room and he said in a whisper, "I'm going to tell you about the most terrible thing of all." What he told me was by no means the most terrible thing of all. He told me that he had been taken to a factory where books were pulped, and with great force and his classical command of language he described how hefty girls sat there tearing off the covers. And this great destruction of books went on day after day. "It's terrible," he said.

I was depressed by the conversation and said, "Yes." To which he said, "And suppose this is only the beginning?"

This was very much one of his themes: intellectuals, people who read books and think and have minds of their own, on the one hand; and elemental primitiveness, on the other. And he talked about those girls the way Dovzhenko† saw them in *Earth*—as a blind force of nature issuing from the earth.

This was one of our last meetings.

I do not know what he wrote after this. He always said that he aimed at simplicity. His simplicity was not of the kind that

---

* Microphones were often hidden in telephones by the secret police.
† Alexander Petrovich Dovzhenko (1894–   ), film director who was awarded the title of "People's Artist." His most famous film, *Earth* (1931), deals with the difficulties of collectivization in the Ukraine.

was required: it was a simplicity born of complexity—not a substitute for it. (*Applause.*)

But I wish to say one thing: he was a great writer. I'm not saying this [only] because I still love him. I first got to know him in 1926 and I last saw him in the summer of 1938. But— to use the language of the literary experts—objectively speaking, he is the glory of Soviet literature. (*Applause.*)

We are in the House of Writers. We are all writers or lovers of literature; we are all in one way or another concerned with Soviet literature.

What does it mean, rehabilitation? It's [not just] a matter [of withdrawing] the absurd accusations which were written down in his file, things which surprised [even] the public prosecutor. These accusations really were absurd. This we have known for a long time.

Those of us who are still alive have a duty to Babel and the reading public. Isn't it astonishing that in the country of the language in which he wrote he is published ten times less than in the other Socialist countries and in the West? This is really terrible. (*Applause.*)

Yesterday I got a letter from Iwaszkiewicz.* Knowing that this meeting was going to take place, he writes many nice things about Babel and says that in 1961 the Polish translation of the Babel volume that came out in Moscow in 1957 was reprinted twice, and that another small edition of 20,000 copies has just appeared and was sold out the same day. But here he was published once in 1957—and that was that, nothing more can be done.

Isn't it terrible that we asked permission to hold this meeting in the Polytechnic Museum but were told, "No, only in the

---

* Well-known Polish writer, secretary of the Polish Union of Writers and editor of the important literary journal *Twórczość*.

House of Writers."* And there was a line of people on the street who couldn't get in. He was a writer of the Revolution, a writer loved by our people.

If he were still alive, if he had had no talent, his collected works would have been reprinted a dozen times over. (*Prolonged applause.*)

Don't think that I am just letting off steam. What I want is for us writers at last to take a hand in this business, to tell the publishing houses† to reissue Babel, to organize symposiums on him. Why is it that the Poles and the Czechs can arrange such meetings, while here, if it weren't for Zhuravlyov,‡ to whom I am deeply grateful on Babel's behalf, people wouldn't even know his name. People have even confused him [Zhuravlyov] with Babel. There is a whole new generation which doesn't know him—surely it is not asking too much to make the stories which Gorky liked so much available to the public. After all, we writers, out of respect for the reader, are not only concerned about writing better; we also want people to read good writers. That is our duty. If we writers don't do something about this, then who will?

Earlier, I wanted to quote what many foreign writers have said about Babel, the things that have been written about him, things that have just been sent [to me?], and also what I remember people saying about him.

I remember what Hemingway said to me in a hotel in Madrid. He had just read Babel for the first time, and he said, "I have never believed that arithmetic is important for the appreciation of literature. I have been criticized for writing too

---

* The Polytechnic Museum has the largest public auditorium in Moscow. The House of Writers, on Vorovsky Street, in Moscow, is the headquarters of the Union of Soviet Writers.

† As publishing houses are state-controlled in the Soviet Union, the printing of books depends on the allocation of paper and other resources.

‡ D. N. Zhuravlyov, leading Soviet actor who also participated in the evening honoring Babel's seventieth birthday.

concisely, but I find that Babel's style is even more concise than mine, which is more wordy. It shows what can be done. Even when you've got all the water out of them, you can still clot the curds a little more."

When Isaac Emmanuelovich went up to the platform at the Paris Congress° and, without any notes at all, spoke of what people read in our kolkhozes, he gave a vivid idea of the spiritual freshness of our people. When he had finished, the elderly, long-haired Heinrich Mann jumped from his seat and said to me, "Can you introduce me to Babel?"

I know of no country and of no writers of any stature who have not felt the power of Babel's sincerity and humanity, and who do not love him. If there are any such people, they could only be vicious enemies of ours.

And so, seventy years have passed . . . It's as though we were celebrating his birthday. I am willing to get up on my hind legs and beg like a dog in front of all the necessary organizations in order to get them to reissue his works, which have become very hard to find, though there are now no obstacles [to their republication]. Is it a question of paper? Very well, I will put off one of my own books. We cannot be indifferent to the impatience of people eager to learn about this writer who perished long ago. It is difficult to understand why doors

---

° In 1935 a Congress for the Defense of Culture and Peace took place in Paris. Ilya Ehrenburg in his *Memoirs* writes: "The Soviet Delegation arrived, without Babel. The French writers who had organized the Congress requested our Embassy to include the author of *Red Cavalry* in the delegation. Babel arrived late, on the second or the third day, I think. He was due to speak immediately. He reassured me with a smile, 'I'll find something to say.' This is how I described Babel's speech in *Izvestia:* Babel did not read his speech, he spoke gaily and in masterly French for fifteen minutes, entertaining the audience with several unwritten stories. People laughed but at the same time they realized that under cover of those amusing stories the essence of our people and of our culture was being conveyed to them; 'this collective farmer has bread, he has a house, he even has a decoration. But it's not enough for him. Now he wants poetry to be written about him.'" (From Ilya Ehrenburg, *Memoirs: 1921–41*, pp.116–117.)

were shut and why [we have to] wait until the celebration of his eightieth anniversary before anybody can get in.

I would like all writers to help in bringing one thing to pass: that our people should read Babel. Isn't there enough paper to publish one little book? It is not a question of publishing a huge "collected works." The paper must be found. (*Applause.*)

Everything I have heard [about him], from all kinds of people, adds up to the same thing. He had a wide range of friends, even in Paris, where he did not live all that long. Among them were wine merchants, jockeys, taxi drivers (not only the brother of Lev Venyaminovich [Nikulin]), and, of course, M. Triolet—the first husband of Elsa Triolet*—who was very fond of the races. The way Babel used to talk about horses! His judgments were always smiling, his malice was always humorous. He always toned down things that were too terrible.

I have been comparing his diary of the Red Cavalry [period] with the stories. He scarcely changed any names, the events are all practically the same, but everything is illuminated with a kind of wisdom. He is saying: this is how it was. This is how the people were—they did terrible things and they suffered, they played cruel tricks on others and they died. He made his stories out of the facts and phrases hastily jotted down in his notebook.

But I've talked too long. I was moved by the words of all those who knew Isaac Emmanuelovich and by the way they have been heard—not only by the people here in the hall but by those standing outside, in the corridors and in the street. I am glad for Isaac Emmanuelovich. I am glad that Antonina Nikolayevna and Babel's daughter Lidya are here and have heard and seen how much he is loved.

---

* Elsa Triolet (1896–   ), wife of the French Communist writer Louis Aragon, and a novelist in her own right.

LEV NIKULIN

Years of Our Life: Babel, on His Seventieth Birthday*

❁

H E LOVED to play tricks on people. Sometimes he did it for fun and sometimes for a serious purpose—to get to know somebody better, for instance.

We attended the same school for a time in Odessa—the Nicholas I Commercial College. It was odd that the merchants of Odessa had chosen as patron of their school a czar who took such a poor view of commerce. Babel was one class behind me, but I remember him as a bespectacled boy in a rather shabby school coat and a battered cap with a green band and badge depicting Mercury's staff.

When we met sixteen years later at Vasily Reginin's, the journalist who edited the magazine *Thirty Days*, Reginin didn't give Babel's name but introduced him as someone prominent in the management of the country's economy. In his navy-blue coat of the type that was still sentimentally called a "French," Babel simply didn't look the part. Furthermore, Reginin soon brought the conversation around to literature and asked whether I had read "Salt," "The Death of Dolgushov," and other stories from *Red Cavalry*. At this point

---

* "*Gody nashei zhizni. I. Babel (k 70-letiyu so dnya rozhdeniya)*" was first published in the literary journal *Moskva*, No. 7, 1964, pp. 182–187.

Babel interrupted: "Don't you remember me? I remember you. You played Tartuffe when we put on Molière at school." I said that that had been the first and last time I had appeared in a play. "I thought you would become an actor," he said. "Well, and don't you think I look like an important official?" I said I thought he had played the part badly but as though he meant it. Babel laughed.

Reginin was an excellent conversationalist and told many amusing stories that evening. So we didn't have much time to reminisce about the past or talk about the present and the future. As he was leaving, Babel said: "We must meet again."

As it turned out, we next saw each other abroad, in Paris, in the autumn of 1927. On his first visit to Paris, Babel seemed to melt into the background of the city. He soon lost interest in Montparnasse, the Coupole, and the Dôme, and would often come to see us in the Avenue de Wagram, or rather in the rue Bréa, where, in the cheap Hôtel Tilsit, all kinds of people lived—Russians and various foreigners of no fixed occupation.

Babel was not in the habit of phoning beforehand. He once came when I was out, and knocked at the door of my neighbor, an actress with the Chauves-Souris—right then, Baliyev's cabaret was in Paris on tour and was about to leave for New York. A man's voice answered Babel's knock. Babel went in, and there was a young man there who said: "You want Tamochka? She's at rehearsal."

"And who are you?" Babel asked.

"I'm her suitor."

Babel later spoke with amusement of this encounter. He got to know the young couple and forecast a brilliant acting career for the young man. That's the way it turned out—he is now a famous character actor in the American cinema. And my neighbor is his wife. They both remember Babel with warmth and affection.

In Paris he sent me notes via the so-called *pneumatique*, for example:

Dear Lev Venyaminovich,

I am really quite ill. I can't sleep nights, I have a terrible cold, my eye is all puffed up and full of matter. All in all, I am decomposing even less aesthetically than the Paris bourgeoisie. I long to see you. I'm very bad company, of course. As soon as I get better, I'll come over and see you. I'll give you due notice by letter.

Your Babel

14/ix/27

But he never gave warning, he just came. We went for walks around Paris in autumn. He said: "We must thank God that we were taught by that Frenchman, Vadon. He taught us to chatter in French, otherwise we would be like deaf-mutes here." He was an amusing person to be with. Whenever he came across something funny, he would stop and laugh for a long time, sometimes gasping for breath—his heart gave him trouble.

Once in Montmartre we stopped in front of a house with a certain reputation in the night life of Paris. At nighttime the place was full of life, but we happened to come across it in the morning. The windows were wide open and one could clearly see all the tawdry trappings and the mirrors. "What do you think," Babel asked. "Do they keep books in this place?" "I should think so," I replied. "It's a commercial enterprise and they have to pay taxes." "It would be fascinating to study the entries in the books. They would make a chapter in a good novel."

In the Hôtel Tilsit there was a Russian taxi driver called Volodya—he had been a student, then a lieutenant in the army, and during World War I had somehow got from the Rumanian front to Paris. In autumn, in bad weather, he didn't have much business and he'd drive us round the city at half price. We would go along slowly, stopping by the Seine, or in the Latin Quarter, on the ancient little square at the back of the Panthéon. At that time Paris still had gaslights, which cast an eerie, phosphorescent glow on the houses and the bare trees on the boulevards. We made these nocturnal trips two or three times: "taking a ride with Volodya," we called it. Some years later Babel said to me sadly: "How nice it would be to go for a ride with Volodya again."

On one of those nights out in Paris, we found ourselves on the boulevard Rochechouart and stopped near the Black Ball nightclub. We went in and a pretty, dark-skinned woman joined us at our table. She turned out to be a Moroccan girl who danced with a live python at the Casino de Paris. Babel questioned her closely about her earnings, about what the python ate and how long it slept. Afterwards we dropped the Moroccan girl off at the hotel where she lived.

"Do you know beauty when you see it?" Babel asked. "What are they waiting for, these French lovers of women? Such a beautiful girl and she has to work in that awful hole!"

"She'll be all right," Volodya said gloomily. "All she needs is for her lucky number to come up."

Her lucky number did come up. Two years later her photograph was in *France-Soir*. She had everything: jewels, an automobile, even a villa on the Riviera. Her photograph and story were published in the newspaper after her death. She had been stabbed by a jealous lover.

In a café near the Gare Saint-Lazare, Babel pointed out to me a tall, very beautiful, strangely silent woman. She was in a low-cut but crumpled and faded evening dress. "Just like Hélène Bezukhov, isn't she?" Babel remarked. It was true: one could have imagined the beautiful Hélène Bezukhov* to be just like her, but her price was the same as that of all the

---

* A prominent character in Tolstoy's *War and Peace*.

lonely women near the Gare Saint-Lazare at four o'clock in the
morning with a cold rain coming down.

Once I suddenly got the following note from him:

Dear boy:

This is how things have worked out. I went off on the spur of
the moment—just as I would like to die. Boy, it just happened
by sheer luck! If you are still in the hotel, and if you are not
coming to Marseilles, drop me a line . . .

He went on to urge me to come to Marseilles, and I wrote
to ask how long he was going to be there. I soon got a reply:

Not only shall I not leave Marseilles by November 1; I shall
never leave it at all. Whenever you come, you will find me here.

If you arrive in the evening (there is a train that gets into Marseilles at ten in the evening), I will meet you. Let me know
what day you are coming and by what train.

But he did leave Marseilles after all:

Business calls me to Paris. Waiting for you is like waiting for the
Second Coming. So now you can damn well wait for me in the
Hôtel Tilsit.

He spoke to me about Marseilles with great enthusiasm,
saying that it was like an Odessa which had blossomed out on
a world scale. He was delighted by the neighborhood around
the Old Port—the ancient houses; the women, aged by vice,
sidling out of their tiny rooms; the sailors of all races and
nations. It was all as described by Maupassant. Incidentally,
this quarter has ceased to exist: it was destroyed by bombs in
World War II. The whole area has been rebuilt in modern
style, with high-rent houses.

In Paris, Babel lived on a street called Villa Chauvelot. We
joked about how his Moscow friends thought he was living in
a luxury villa.

At the end of 1927 I returned to Moscow, and during 1928 we wrote to each other quite a lot. In February I got the following letter from him:

Dear Lev Venyaminovich:

Do me a favor and go see *Sunset,* and then try to find the time to let me have a description of the whole disgraceful business. I have just got the play as published by *The Circle (Krug).* It's scandalous. The sense is completely distorted by misprints. Poor play! . . . Of all the events that deserve to be noted, the first is the wonderful, unbelievable spring here. People were right to say how fine the spring is in Paris . . .

Up to February I'd been working well, and then I got on to writing something quite extraordinary, but yesterday at 11:30 in the evening I realized that it was absolute, hopeless trash, and pretentious into the bargain . . . It means a total waste of six weeks' work. Today I am still very upset, but tomorrow I shall think about how one learns from one's mistakes. . . .

I told Babel about *Sunset* and, if my memory serves me, I had to disappoint him.

Every work of his attracted attention. After the Odessa stories it was fashionable for a time to talk in the language of Benya Krik. Leo Tolstoy praised Kuprin* for his ability to handle bastardized language with such skill. Babel had a similarly brilliant command of the language of the Odessa suburbs. This language is a headache for Western translators. Babel's epic tale of Odessa *bindyuzhniki* (draymen) is exciting to Western readers—for them it is something exotic. In *Sunset,* however, our public was interested not in the exotic element but in the eternal theme of approaching old age. Babel had a foreboding that it would be a failure in the theater and knew that it would not be played as it should be. All this worried him, and in his next letter from Paris he again wrote

---

* Alexander Ivanovich Kuprin (1870–1938), a leading Russian novelist and short-story writer of the early twentieth century.

about the delightful spring and then turned once more to the question of his play:

No, it's wrong to run it down—this is a fine city. The only trouble is that it's very set in its ways . . . In April I shall probably go to Italy, to see Gorky: the patriarch is summoning me urgently and there's no refusing him. I shall stay there until Gorky leaves for Russia . . . Incidentally, about *Sunset:* I am proud that I foresaw its failure down to the last detail. If I ever write a play again (and no doubt I shall), I will sit in at all the rehearsals, strike up an acquaintance with the producer's wife, and later get myself a job on the *Evening Moscow* or the *Evening Red,* and the play will be called *At the Turning Point* or, say, *Broad is the Land.* Slowly though it may be, I am composing new works . . . I have been ill with the flu, but now I am better and feel a buoyancy of spirit which is even somewhat dangerous—I fear I may burst! Dear friend, Lev Venyaminovich, do not forget me and God will not forsake you! . . . It's very good to get your letters. And there must be some news from Moscow . . .

To all appearances, Babel bore his misfortunes and failures with fortitude. Nobody knows why the "extraordinary" thing he had been working on for six weeks did not come off. He does not exaggerate when he speaks of the torments of his work, of all his wasted days, months, even years. Perhaps he was too much of a perfectionist. "My writing is just too high-flown somehow," Babel wrote in one of his letters to me.

He observed life greedily, trying to get inside the skin of people in the West. On August 7, 1928, he wrote me from Ostend:

I've seen a lot of things in my time, but I could never have imagined in my wildest dreams such a glittering, stupefying Sodom as this. I am writing to you from the terrace of a casino. But I just do my writing here. I shall go and eat on the fantastic fishermen's wharf where the Flemings make their nets and fish is

dried on the street. I shall drink your health in Scotch ale and
eat *moules frites*. Be well.

Yours,

I. Babel

Babel was an easy person to be with; one didn't have to
show off or carry on pompous conversations about literature.
We once had a long talk about Odessa, about the Odessan
petty bourgeoisie. Babel not only knew their language, he
knew their mean-mindedness, their fanatical stupidity and
greed. They didn't all live in the suburbs. Many of them were
small or middling officials who read only the Black Hundred*
Voice of Russia (*Russkaya rech*). In Odessa there were even
Black Hundred secondary schools: Sinitsyn's and the Fifth.
But there was also a strong working class in the city, workers
and sailors, and a democratic intelligentsia. It was odd that the
most rabid Black Hundred types, including the brute of a city
governor and the mayor, should have made their home in a
city like this.

We were mere youths in 1907–10, but we were well up on
the political situation. And when many years later Babel talked
about Odessa, he had a very clear, vivid picture of the state of
affairs in his native city after 1905. But in his Odessa stories he
created, as an artist, an imaginary town, which only he could
see, with hyperbolic images and scenes of everyday life. Was
it really like that? I don't think so. The gangster Mishka the
Jap† from the Civil War days was projected into the Benya
Krik of the post-1905 period. This is really an unnatural blend.
During the Civil War, Odessa changed hands more than once:
it was occupied by foreigners and by Denikin's‡ army. Black-

---

* See note 3 to "Odessa," p. 195.
† Nickname of a famous Odessa gangster.
‡ Anton Ivanovich Denikin (1872–1947), Russian general who from
1918 to 1920 led the anti-Bolshevik forces.

marketeering on a vast scale, and foreign intervention, cor-
rupted the population, particularly the young people. The
petty bourgeois who read the *Voice of Russia* and were often
members of the Union of the Russian People* were on top of
the world. But there were instances of real heroism and courage in the working-class underground; there was Jeanne Labourbe, for instance, and Lastochkin, and the mutiny of the
French sailors.†

When we talked about this, Babel was quite seriously upset
that what he saw in his mind's eye was not this real-life
Odessa but the one he had created in his Odessa stories.

In one of his letters Babel wrote:

> Come in August—I shall be in Paris until then. I am unlikely to
> finish my "labor of Sisyphus" before August. It's very interesting
> here at the moment—quite extraordinarily interesting, one might
> say; the election campaign is on and in the last week I have got
> to know more about the French and France than in all the
> preceding months I have spent here.
>
> All in all, I can see things much more clearly now, and I hope
> that by the time I have to leave I shall have in my heart and mind
> something worthwhile to bring back. Be of good cheer, and
> work hard!! Your postcards, to put it in plain words, warm the
> cockles of my heart, and I beg you to send them as often as
> possible.

Babel was making a close study of life in France; he had
decided to write about it and perhaps was already doing so

---

* An ultra-nationalist, anti-Semitic organization.
† Jeanne Labourbe was a French schoolteacher who went to Russia
before the Revolution, took part in revolutionary activities, and organized
a French Communist group in Moscow after the October Revolution.
Early in 1919 she was sent to Odessa to organize propaganda among
French sailors of the Entente forces then occupying Odessa. In March
1919 she was arrested and shot, together with ten members of the
Bolshevik underground, of whom Lastochkin was presumably one.

and hoped to bring back images of the country in his "heart and mind." This was probably the "labor of Sisyphus" to which he refers. Over and over again he talked about the torment of work. Yet newspapers and magazines in Moscow were waiting for him to produce pieces for them. I no longer remember which publication it was that asked me to cable him a request for a fragment of whatever he was working on. Babel cabled back:

Impossible. Letter follows. Babel.

And, in fact, I did get a letter, dated August 30, 1928:

I still haven't put my things in a fit shape for publication. This will still take some time. I'm having quite a lot of trouble with these things. To work at speed and by such methods I should need, as you once rightly observed, at least Yasnaya Polyana,* but I haven't got it. In fact, I haven't got a bean, and I'm not even going to try to make any! I have quite deliberately condemned myself for a stretch of several years to a penniless and happy-go-lucky existence. It was in view of this high-minded resolution that I most regretfully (it really did make me very sad) cabled you that I cannot let the newspaper have anything. I shall be returning to Russia in October. I don't know where I shall live; I shall go somewhere as cheap and out-of-the-way as possible. All I know is that it won't be Moscow. I really have nothing at all to do there (in Moscow). . . My time here is now coming to an end and I spend all day wandering around Paris; I have only now begun to know the place. I have seen Isaac Rabinovich, and they say that Nikitin† was here, but we seem to have missed each other—though perhaps I may still see him.

---

* Yasnaya Polyana ("Clear Meadow") was the family estate of the Tolstoys, about a hundred miles south of Moscow.

† Isaac Moiseyevich Rabinovich (1894–1961) was a well-known Soviet set designer. Nikolai Nikolayevich Nikitin (1897–   ) is a novelist and playwright.

One bit of news: Annenkov* is in very bad shape: he has a large, nasty tubercular growth inside him. Yesterday he had an operation in the clinic where Doyen† used to work. We were very worried about whether he would live, but the operation seems to have gone off well. The doctors say he will get better. Poor Annenkov, he has had a very bad time. Drop him a line to cheer him up a little.

Well, see you soon, dear comrade. It gives me joy to write: very soon.

Babel came home to Moscow, and we began to see a good deal of each other. I lived near the race track and Babel loved horses and horse racing and used to hobnob with the jockeys. In the mornings he would come and watch the horses being exercised. It was something to see the enthusiasm with which he talked about a horse called Petrushka: "He's a genius," he'd say. He used to say that only racing people and cavalrymen really understood horses.

It was not at the race track but on the street somewhere that Babel introduced me to his closest friend, the Civil War hero Dmitry Arkadyevich Shmidt. On first acquaintance, Shmidt seemed dour and uncommunicative, but later I was struck by his particular and very intelligent brand of humor. He never spoke about the war or his own exploits, except to say, on one occasion, that he spent all his war years (he had been awarded the St. George's Cross in World War I) "rotting in bandages." Although he was a soldier to the marrow of his bones, there was nothing at all swashbuckling about him. He was a real Bolshevik soldier who had joined the party in 1915. His humor and love of literature, his learning and cultivation—which he

---

* Yuri Pavlovich Annenkov (1889–   ), writer and artist known for his portraits of Russian political and literary figures and his film costumes and décor. Emigrated to Paris in 1922. For his interesting memoir of Babel, see *People and Portraits: A Tragic Cycle* (*Dnevnik moikh vstrech; tsikl tragedii*), New York, 1966.

† Eugène-Louis Doyen (1859–1916), well-known French surgeon.

carried very lightly—were combined with the polish of a military leader. In the last years of his life he commanded a tank brigade.

Could we have imagined then, at the end of the twenties, that Babel and Shmidt would meet the same fate during the "cult of personality" in Stalin's time?

Babel would sometimes disappear from Moscow for long periods. At the end of 1931 he was living out at Molodenovo, at the stud farm there. Once we were supposed to go out to see him—"we" being Dmitry Shmidt; Tsypin, the director of the Federation publishing house; and myself. It was a rather difficult journey, since the roads around Moscow in those days left much to be desired and the automobiles were pretty feeble and had seen better days. Babel had written to tell us how to get there:

> I'll expect you all on the third, around two o'clock. That is what I agreed with Tsypin. Here is the way you come: Take the Mozhaisk road to Perkhushkovo and turn off there to Uspenskoye. I'll be waiting for you at the stud farm at two o'clock. The road to the Uspenskoye state farm is all right; then it will be rough going for about a mile and a half. I shall be waiting for you with the deputy manager, Kurlandsky, or with Penkin, the trainer.
>
> I'll try to phone you tomorrow, or the day after. I have provisions and vodka—if you want delicatessen and white bread, bring them with you . . .
>
> Regards—the warmest I am capable of—to E. G.
>
> Yours,
I. Babel
>
> Molodenovo
30/x/31

For some reason we didn't go after all. I can only regret this. We were not all that young by then and we were not wholly absorbed in our work, but we had the feeling that everything still lay ahead of us and that there would be no end of chances to see this good, intelligent, gifted man. But this opportunity of seeing him in a different surrounding and among new people was missed. . . . It was the same in France, when I didn't go see him in Marseilles—though it was not my fault that we didn't go out to see him that time in Molodenovo. I think Tsypin let us down. But now it makes me sad to think of it—one cannot recapture the past, and Babel has left us forever.

On his visits to Moscow, Babel did not much like the company of his fellow writers, particularly if they indulged in malicious gossip, or even if they spoke highly of him, for that matter. He seemed to get along very well with all kinds of people, but that was only how it looked. As soon as someone ceased to interest him, he would disappear.

He liked to talk with Olesha.° The only thing that bothered him was that during conversation at the table Yuri Karlovich would reach for the bottle rather often. Babel would say with a sigh: "Don't overdo it, Yura . . . I'll soon have no one to talk with."

He was always intrigued by celebrities. In Paris he got to know Chaliapin, and it was to him that Chaliapin said: "My life hasn't worked out." (Though, actually, he sometimes said this to other people as well.) Babel also met Ivan Bunin.† I don't remember what Babel said to me about him, but Bunin saw fit to make a rude, slighting reference to Babel in his

---

° See note on page 219.

† Leading writer and lyric poet (1870–1953) who emigrated to France in 1918. In 1933 he became the first Russian to receive the Nobel Prize for Literature. His *Memoirs* (Paris, 1950) show that his strong distaste for everything Soviet often distorted his literary judgments. Of Babel he wrote: "One of the most revolting blasphemers was Babel . . . I remember one story of Babel's in which among other things there was mention of a statue of the Virgin in a Catholic church, but I have tried to put it out of my mind: for the vile way in which her breasts were spoken of here he deserved to have his head chopped off, particularly since, as it seems, he was completely healthy and normal in the ordinary sense of these words." (*Memoirs* [*Vospominanya*], pp. 47–48)

Memoirs, which came out, incidentally, in 1950, by which time news of Babel's fate had reached Paris. But Babel was in good company: Blok and Mayakovsky also come in for abuse.

On one other occasion fate brought Babel and me together while we were abroad. This time it was in Italy, at Gorky's house in Sorrento. It happened like this: in February 1933 I went to Turkey and wrote to Babel from Istanbul about my travels. On February 22 I got the following reply from him:

Dear L. V.

I cannot tell you how pleased I was to get your card and how glad I am, with all my heart, for you . . . After all this time. Although I haven't written I think of you often, particularly when I walk along the Avenue de Wagram . . . Paris is a great city and it's grown even better . . . The Americans and the English with their big money have gone away; Paris is French again—which makes it even more poetic, expressive, and mysterious . . . I fear we shall not meet in Montparnasse. At the beginning of the summer I shall be in Moscow and in March I want to go to Italy. Perhaps I should take in Turkey as well and return via Constantinople? Is Italy on your itinerary? Let me know. Write me about what goes on in Russia. We had a reading here of your feuilleton on Pilnyak* and nearly died laughing . . . I have a three-and-a-half-year-old offspring here—a jolly, amusing, mischievous creature.†

Ehrenburg is rich—the Americans, for the umpteenth time, have bought the film rights for his *Jeanne Ney.* I, on the contrary, am poor. Do I have any friends in our embassy in Turkey? . . .

Let me hear from you very soon . . .

Yours,

I. Babel

---

* Boris Pilnyak is the pseudonym of Boris Vogau (1894–1941?), one of the most original Soviet writers of the twenties. His novel *The Naked Year* (1922) made him famous. Like his friend Babel, he was a victim of the Stalin purges of the late thirties.

† I remember a jolly, amusing, mischievous father.

Almost simultaneously I got a letter from Gorky inviting me to go to see him in Sorrento.

I arrived in Sorrento late at night. In the morning I opened the door onto the terrace and stood looking out in awe and wonderment at the Bay of Naples and the mountains, when suddenly I heard a familiar laugh and a voice saying: "This is all I needed!" It was Babel standing at a window on the second floor of the hotel.

Also visiting Gorky were Samuel Yakovlevich Marshak* and the painter Vasily Nikolayevich Yakovlev. I won't repeat what has been said in various books about those three weeks in Sorrento, about our walks on the grounds of the Il Sorito villa, our excursion to Capri, the long talks over dinner in Gorky's house, and the way Gorky read us his story "They're Coming," which Babel liked so much.

As we went back late at night to our hotel after this reading, Babel said of Gorky, fondly and with some wonderment: "We shall never know what world fame is. Gorky does, but he is just the same as he was when he began. Just think what some other people would be like in his place . . ." And he mentioned a most ambitious countryman of ours. "Can you imagine what it would be like? . . . Did you notice how nervous the old man was and how he kept looking around as he read? But 'They're Coming' is in all the editions of his works."

Babel particularly liked this story, and in 1934, in a talk to members of the staff and readers of the magazine *The Shift* (*Smena*), he said of Gorky: "Take his short stories of a page or two in length. They float through the air like songs. Who remembers his story 'They're Coming'? It's very short. Everybody should read it."

Those spring days in Sorrento passed very quickly. Once

---

* Poet and translator (1887–1964) best known for his children's books.

Gorky's son, Maxim Peshkov, took us in his sports car to Amalfi. He drove with terrifying speed over the winding mountain road, and as he took hairpin bends, he would shout back to us, without turning his head, "Now then, you devils, order your coffins!" However, we got back in one piece. "After what we've been through with you," we said, "nothing can frighten us again."

Babel told us how he had once driven at night with Maxim along a road on which there had been an automobile race the day before. Maxim had not taken part, but he felt just as the drivers had no doubt felt during the race: he was delighted at the thought of covering the distance faster than any of them had, and he was quite upset when he found that he had not made as good time as the first ten in the race. This was touching in a childish way, but one can imagine the feelings of his passenger while the car balanced over precipices as it was rounding corners!

We made a trip to Capri. This picturesque spot is associated with Russian literature and with Gorky; Lenin spent several days there with him.

The sea was rather rough that day. The little steamer plunged down into the troughs or rode up on the crests of the waves, and although the island looked quite close, it took us quite a while to get there.

It was very quiet on the island, there was a warm drizzle, the orange and lemon trees and the cypresses were absolutely still. We went and stood for a moment by the house where Gorky had lived. The gates were shut tight. The rain stopped, people came out into the streets, music started playing in the cafés, and we heard English being spoken . . . The evening found us at the apartment of a doctor, a Russian by descent. We were in his surgery, with its instruments and test tubes. He was a young man and had been born in Italy. He spoke

Russian with a strong Italian accent. On the table in his room we saw the latest issue of the journal *Communist International,* and a volume of Lenin's works. We pointed out that that wasn't safe, that one must not forget that Mussolini was in power.

I mention this meeting because thirty years later I happened to see the Italian magazine *Il Mondo* of January 15, 1957. In it there was an article *Babel a Capri* by Roberto Pane—the young doctor whom we had visited on Capri in 1933. The article was about Babel, his gift as a writer and his personality.

From Sorrento I went to Paris and after two months there returned to Moscow. Babel also went back to Paris and in July 1933 I had a disturbing letter from him. In Moscow there was malicious gossip, mainly in literary circles, about the excessive length of his stay abroad. They knew that Babel's first wife had decided to remain abroad with her relatives and that Babel had a daughter in Paris. He evidently knew all about this talk and in his letter he answers the scandalmongers:

> If only my friends would send me the money for my fare, or even a railroad ticket. I wrote about this five months ago, but nobody answered. What does this mean? It means that I have been left to my own devices in strange and hostile surroundings in which it is impossible for an honest Soviet citizen to earn his livelihood. When I came here, I thought that Yevgenia Borisovna* would have enough money for the return journey. But our American uncle is broke and *misère noire* has set in—debts and so on. The humiliating and absurd thing is that, as someone who has no personal needs and is ill-equipped to ask for favors, I am nevertheless forced to do precisely that, but since it goes against the grain, and against my pride, I do it badly. My life is split-

* Babel's wife, who lived in France from 1925 until her death in 1957. The "American uncle" was her brother, who had emigrated to the United States in 1919.

ting in two and I have to make agonizing decisions. I'm not asking for sympathy, but it would be a good thing if I had the understanding of my comrades.

So much for "the world at large." Now about myself. I am living terribly, and every day's postponement is agony for me; somehow or other I've managed to put together a very brief *exposé*. If they like it and pay me, I will leave this week. If not (it's scarcely done in the Pathé manner!), then . . . then I just don't know what I'll do, except perhaps declare myself bankrupt, ask the Embassy to give me a rail ticket home, and flee my creditors . . .

Voilà, life is hard. I'm desperately anxious to be in Moscow on August 10, otherwise my long-cherished plans will collapse. So, trusting in "God's help," *à bientôt,*

Yours fondly,
I. B.

Ehrenburg was in London and became ill there. Now he's in Sweden.

The "agonizing decision" Babel had to make was to part for what he knew would be a long time (forever, it turned out) with his daughter and his family.* The idea of not going home did not, of course, occur to him, and it is clear that settling down in the West would not have suited Babel. As a writer he was anxious to know everything he could about the West, but he could not do without the hectic, helter-skelter life of the country that was dearest of all to him.

Gorky, in Babel's own phrase, had sent him out "into the world." Babel spent the revolutionary years under the stern discipline of wartime Communism and had been through the school of the Red Cavalry . . . Wherever he lived, he remained a Soviet writer; however original and inimitable, he was nevertheless a Soviet writer.

---

* During the summer of 1935, Babel visited his family in Paris for what turned out to be the last time. See footnote on p. 236.

He had an insatiable hunger for people. Among his friends were engineers, factory directors, party officials, workers, kolkhoz chairmen, soldiers . . . Where else could he have met such people, such characters tempered by the storm and struggle of the greatest revolution the world had ever known? . . . I am sure that in the last years of his life, though no longer free, he continued to study people, their characters, their language, their bitter thoughts.

Babel wrote all these letters abroad, in Paris, Marseilles, Ostend, but there is also the letter from Molodenovo, a little place near Moscow which was not easy to get to in those days. He knew and loved life in Russia, he liked to live "off the beaten track" and preferred this to life in the city.

I have kept these letters for more than thirty years and I reread the last one with grief and pain.

Babel disappeared from our midst, as many of our comrades did, but he left an indelible, I would say a brilliant, mark on our literature. It was not his fault that he was unable to sing his song to the end.

In June of this year Babel would have been seventy. And if I had not written these pages about him, I would have been tormented by a sense of having failed in my duty.

GEORGY MUNBLIT

Reminiscences of Babel*

❁

T HERE IS nothing in the world more difficult than describing
the appearance of a person so that a reader can picture
him as he really looks. It is particularly difficult to describe
what Babel looked like. Everything about him seemed ordinary
enough: his stocky figure and short neck, his broad, kindly
face, and the high forehead, which was frequently creased by
wrinkles. But the overall effect was quite out of the ordinary.
This was felt by everybody who had any close contact with
him.

His quizzical smile and screwed-up eyes were only the ex-
ternal signs of his attitude to everything around him. In fact,
his attitude was invariably one of greedy and well-meaning
curiosity. He was, it always seemed to me, extraordinarily
shrewd and had the ability to see right through everything,
but this shrewdness inclined him not to skepticism but to good-
natured astonishment. Evidently he found cause for this not
on the surface of things but in their depths, which concealed
pleasant surprises invisible to unobservant people.

Our first meeting was, to begin with, entirely about a matter
of business. It happened in 1932, or perhaps a little later.

* "Isaac Emmanuelovich Babel (iz vospominanii)" was first published
in 1964 in the Soviet literary magazine The Banner, No. 8. The text has
been cut in translation, and such cuts are indicated by brackets.

In the editorial offices of *The Banner,* where I then worked, it had become known that Babel had written a film script. He hadn't published anything for a long time, and the idea of getting new work of his—even something intended for the cinema—was a very tempting prospect for us.

We argued at length about who should negotiate with Isaac Emmanuelovich, and at last the choice fell on me. The reason was that I had recently published an article on Babel's stories in the *Literary Gazette,* and it was thought that I was the most likely to be able to get on good terms with him.

Our negotiations began over the phone and it took me a long time to explain to Babel where I was phoning from and for what reason. When he at last understood what it was all about, he said outright that he had no intention of publishing his film script.

I then began to enumerate all the advantages and joys our proposal would bring him if he decided to accept it. He didn't interrupt me and for some reason I suddenly sensed that he was pondering not what I was telling him but something quite different. When I had exhausted all my arguments, I stopped and listened to the crackling and rustling noises so well known to anyone who has had to conduct difficult negotiations over the phone. For a moment I even thought that Babel had hung up. But then I heard his soft, slightly lisping voice.

"Come over and let's have a talk," he said slowly, obviously still lost in thought, and he began to spell out the address. The next day, in the morning, I rang at the door of a tiny, two-story house in a side street near the Pokrovsky Gates. Babel himself opened the door and showed me into a large room—the dining room, by the looks of it—on the ground floor. Here Babel gave me a chair and himself sat down on a large trunk in the corner.

I had heard about this trunk before. It was said that Babel kept his manuscripts in it, carefully hiding them from prying eyes and bringing them out only to correct a line or a word, after which the yellowing pages were put back, doomed to lie there undisturbed for many long months, if not years, to come.

Now, seeing the trunk with my own eyes, I finally believed in the truth of the story.

Our conversation at first seemed to me briefer than I would have liked. Babel had evidently thought everything out before I came, and he told me his decision clearly and concisely: he was willing to let *The Banner* have the script, but only for us to have a look at it. It was not possible, in his opinion, to publish it in its present form. This would reflect glory neither on the magazine nor on the author. As regards a contract—if the editors liked the work and felt confident that it would be successfully completed, then he would gladly sign one, since, once he got an advance, he would soon be able to finish it off, without being distracted by other things. We could send for the manuscript in a day or two—by then he would have a copy ready for us.

So the business about which I had come was settled quickly and, as the saying goes, to our mutual satisfaction.

Both of us then fell silent and I got up to leave. Babel peered at me over the top of his spectacles, and seeing that I was casting my gaze around the room, he said: "This is the dining room. I share it with my neighbor." And, anticipating the unspoken question in my eyes, he went on: "My neighbor is a person I could go on talking about for a long time . . . No, he's not a writer. He's an engineer—not just an ordinary one, but an engineer in the higher sense of the word. Sit down, and I'll tell you about him."

I need scarcely say how pleased I was that Babel had suddenly become so communicative.

"I said 'an engineer in the higher sense,'" Babel continued, "but that's not the way to put it. It would be better to say that

he's an engineer to the marrow of his bones—he looks at everything with the eye of an engineer and is always trying to put
things right and make them better. Everything has its en-
gineering side, you see, and that's all he notices. And he can
do anything with his hands. How can I explain it to you?
Well, a few days ago, for instance, as I was leaving the house
in the morning I found Steiner doing something with the lock
on the front door. It looked all right to me, but he thought it
urgently needed repairing. When I came back at midday, I
found him lying on the floor—he was holding the lock over his
head and talking angrily to it. He didn't even look at me,
though I had to step over him to get inside. In a little while
I could hear his voice.

"'You were made by a bad workman,' Steiner was saying to
the lock, 'but I will remake you. Do you hear? I will remake
you so that you will work properly—even when you're badly
screwed in place. What's this habit nowadays of working only
in the wrong position?' He said this in such a way that I almost
thought he was talking with a living being. I would not have
been in the least surprised to hear the lock stick up for itself
or answer back in a thin, metallic voice. But the lock evidently
had nothing to say for itself and it was silent. And an hour
later Steiner knocked on my door, sat down, wiped his forehead with a handkerchief, and said, as though he was con-
tinuing an interrupted conversation: 'Everything's all right.
Now it's working properly. But, let me tell you, the man in
charge of assembling those locks is a scoundrel.' Then he
told me his theory, which explains a lot in life, about the origin
of badly made things. His theory goes like this: There is nobody in the world who would start doing a piece of work with
the intention of knowingly doing a bad job, saying to himself,
for instance: 'I shall now make a bad lock.' But the trouble is
that, starting out on a job with the best of intentions, a weak

person with insufficient sense of responsibility loses heart, and instead of overcoming some snag or other (and all work consists in overcoming snags), he decides that 'it will do as it is.' This is the reason for the preposterous, ugly, and stupid things which make our lives a misery. It makes good sense, don't you think?"

Babel gave me a sidelong look and waited for my reply. I liked engineer Steiner's theory, and I said so. [. . .] Babel himself, perhaps even more than his neighbor, seems to me to have been the personification of a high sense of duty in everything he said and thought, and particularly in what he wrote. Even the end of the story about the film script for *The Banner*, which at first sight might seem to contradict what I say, is actually an excellent confirmation of it.

On the appointed day the manuscript of the scenario was duly received in the editorial office and we immediately began to read it, passing it to each other page by page. This reading took place in one of the two rooms in Herzen House, on Tverskoi Boulevard, that then served as the offices of *The Banner*, and it was done by the young writers who were virtually responsible for producing the magazine.

When we had finished reading, we exchanged embarrassed glances. It wasn't that it was bad or for some reason unpublishable—on the contrary, from this point of view it was completely all right. But it "wasn't Babel"—as one might have said of the work of an artist copying paintings or drawings of the great masters—though every line in the manuscript lying before us had undoubtedly been written by Babel himself.

In painting, even the most casual sketch, a few hasty strokes drawn on a scrap of paper by a great artist, leaves no doubt that it belongs to him: it bears the mark of his personality and conveys something of his genius. In literature, particularly in the case of writers like Babel, who copy out their work over and over again, it is different. Here the writer's individuality of manner becomes clear only when the original draft has been thoroughly gone over and rewritten. [. . .]

Anyway, the manuscript we had just read, though it had undoubtedly been written by Babel, was a draft that did not yet bear the imprint of his manner, his genius, his craftsmanship. As material for a film director to begin work with, it was perfectly all right, but it would scarcely have lent luster to our magazine, as we had thought a work of Babel's might. Realizing this, we were extremely upset. But our oldest, most experienced colleague, who was secretary of the editorial board, smiled indulgently and hastened to console us.

"Don't worry," he said. "Things aren't as bad as all that. We will contract with Babel, and if, as it happens fairly often with him now, he does not deliver, we will simply print the manuscript as is. There's nothing to lose. Do you understand?"

We understood. Although Babel was right in feeling that the script would not add to his laurels or bring him any satisfaction, it was different for the magazine: the publication in *The Banner* of anything by the celebrated, silent author would be a sensation.

So a contract was signed, Babel received an advance, and we began patiently waiting for him to tell us when the revisions were done. A month went by, then another, and there was no word from Babel. I was instructed to find out how things were going and in what issue of the magazine we might expect to carry the film script.

After much hesitation and several peevish reminders from our inflexible secretary, I at last plucked up the courage to telephone Babel and was again invited to visit him in his little house near the Pokrovsky Gates. And so once more I found myself sitting in the large room, which on that autumn day was dark, and this mysterious man was again sitting across from me, with his sly, winning smile, telling me a story. And, as on our first meeting, I was trying to fathom the secret of the diabolic power that made me see everything through his eyes; and, just as before, I couldn't make it out at all.

Perhaps the secret of his charm was in his smile? Or in his eyes, with their merry, observant twinkle, behind the round glasses? No, I don't think it was that. Perhaps the secret was in his astonishing gift of seeing things in his own way and of speaking about them so that, listening to him, you also saw them from unexpected angles and found unexpected meaning in them.

Despite the bleak, not too comfortable room, the wet, nearly bare tree outside the window, and the difficult errand on which I had come, I sat there in the best of moods and could have gone on listening forever to the high-pitched, lisping voice and remained for the rest of my life in this wonderland where he had his being and of which he was now giving me a glimpse. Everything in the world intrigued and amused him and he looked at it all as though through colored glasses that endowed even the most drab objects with a festive magnificence.

I repeatedly reminded myself that I had come on a stern, prosaic mission, and though it was hard for me, I finally spoke the words I had been instructed to speak, which had to be spoken if we were to get Babel's work for *The Banner*. [. . .] You should have seen how frightened Babel looked: his smile suddenly vanished and a worried expression came over his face at the thought that we might carry out our threat to publish his film script just as it was.

"You are still very young," he said sadly, reproachfully, "so young that you have probably never stopped to think what a strange profession this is of ours. We slave away at our desks in complete solitude and while we are working on something we are terrified that somebody might see it, but we pour out all our innermost thoughts and secrets to our readers. So what could be simpler, you ask, than publishing this film script, as the secretary of your editorial board suggests? People will say that it is not up to the standard of my other work, or, on the contrary, that it marks a new phase in my development. How I hate words like that: 'marks a new phase,' 'development'. . . . And then the story I'm writing now will be published, and everything will be fine again. . . . So there's nothing to worry about, eh? First we expose ourselves a little and then we cover up our private parts. Is that the idea?"

"You haven't begun to work on the new version yet?" I asked, with a certain horror in my voice.

"What new version? What are you talking about?"

"The new version of your film script."

"No, I haven't begun. And I'm not going to. I don't like it. I didn't write it to be read, but to be filmed."

"But don't you. . . . Then why did you let us have it?"

"So I could finish my story. Don't you see?"

"No, I don't see. Any magazine would gladly have signed a contract for the story. So why. . . ."

"Why? Because when I've finished it, it will be only about four pages long at the most."

"Typed pages?" I asked, for want of something better to say.

"Yes, typed pages," Babel said with cutting politeness.

We both fell silent. The bare tree outside the window now looked just as it was supposed to: wet, ugly, and sad. And somehow it was darker in the room, darker even than in the street.

"What's to be done then?" I asked this from a sudden, urgent need to find a solution not so much for *The Banner's* as for Babel's sake: for some reason I now had his interests very much at heart.

"God alone knows what's to be done. I suppose I shouldn't

write stories four pages long and spend several months on
them. One should write novels, young man, long novels in in-
stallments, and turn them out quickly, easily, and efficiently."
He fell silent and, resting his arms on the edge of the large
trunk on which he was sitting, he began to drum on it with his
fingers.

"That's not what I meant," I said. "I didn't mean what's to be
done in general, but what's to be done right now. What are
we going to do about *The Banner* and the film script? You see,
if you don't give us something else, they'll print it."

"I don't have anything else at the moment. . . . Listen, suppose I ask your secretary to return my manuscript? It might be,
after all, that I haven't kept a copy to work on?"

Again, I couldn't think what to say. But the silence soon
grew so oppressive that I broke it, feeling the way a man does
who gulps in air after being under water for a long time.

"What do you mean?" I said, averting my eyes.

"I don't mean anything," Babel replied and got up.

I remained sitting. And suddenly, summoning up my courage
but still not looking him in the eye, I said: "Better let me talk
with him. He won't give the manuscript back to you."

Babel looked at me with dismay and shrugged his shoulders.
"Very well then," he said, and after a pause, went on to ask:
"Was it you who wrote that article about my stories in the
Literary Gazette?"

I nodded. It was now difficult for me to speak.

"I no longer remember, but didn't you too use words like
'development' and 'marks a new phase'?" Babel asked with a
smile.

"Perhaps I did. At least I might have," I replied gruffly.

Although I didn't see anything wrong in my offer to help
Babel recover his manuscript, I was deeply ashamed. Later I
realized that there was no reason at all to be ashamed, that

the remarkable story—almost his best—which Babel was then working on (it was the story about the Italian tragic actor Di Grasso) justified anything that might have been done to insure its completion. But that day, as I wandered, after saying goodbye to Babel, along the wet streets and slippery boulevards, and the next morning, when I had a devious but unexpectedly successful conversation with the secretary of the editorial board, I wasn't for a single moment free of that feeling of shame.

I knew that the interests of *The Banner* and my loyalty to it should not override higher, more important motives. Neither was I oblivious to the fact that it was wiser and much more farsighted of us to wait until Babel could let us have a story instead of the script, but even so, I felt that my part in the whole business was despicable. And as for Babel's perfidy—I just tried not to think about it.

I now feel very differently about it all. Having reread his work many times over, having gone through the yellowing pages of his correspondence, having learned that his story "Lyubka the Cossack" was rewritten twenty-six times, and remembering my own encounter with him, I can say with complete certainty that this sly, unfaithful, eternally evasive and mysterious Babel, pursued by creditors from every walk of life, and by editors of every kind of magazine who had unwisely signed contracts with him, and about whose protracted silence in the thirties there were newspaper articles and feuilletons, speeches at writers' conferences, and even, apparently, satirical songs, was a man with an almost morbid sense of responsibility . . . a man who would willingly suffer any deprivation in order not to have to publish something he didn't feel was completely finished, a man for whom service to the cruel god who invented the torment of writing was something immeasurably more important than concern for his own welfare, or even for his reputation as a writer.

And now I shall tell the story of a small miracle [. . .] that Babel performed right before my eyes shortly after the business of the film script.

It all started when Babel phoned me to say that he would like to send us a "budding writer" and asked us to treat him as nicely as possible. . . . The next day the man appeared in our office. He was a very strange "budding writer." He was short and bandy-legged, frail-looking, yet wiry, with a face like parchment, from which it was quite impossible to tell his age. He sidled into the room, proffered me his small hand, which looked like a bird's talon but felt as hard as stone, and laid a thin folder on the table before me. I was overcome with curiosity and as soon as he left I untied the ribbon on the folder and started to read.

The manuscript consisted of several short stories which I now barely remember. I only recall that they were about horses, that they seemed quite undistinguished and were wholly unsuitable for publication. I could not understand what Babel could have seen in them.

I phoned Babel and told him what I thought. He seemed embarrassed. "Very well," he said. "Send the manuscript back to me, if that's not too much trouble, and I'll see what I can do," and he hung up. [. . .]

A few days later the "budding writer" with the bandy-legs came into our office and, without a word, once more set down his manuscript in front of me. I now felt no interest at all and didn't get around to reading it for some time. To my surprise, there were now only two stories in the folder. But when I read them I wanted to run out into the street and tell all my friends and acquaintances about them. My colleagues on the editorial board, who were immediately exposed to my enthusiasm, and who shared it completely, seemed too small an audience.

I must say that there was good reason for my surprise and delight. The stories were now superb. These stories, which two weeks before had seemed so mediocre, were now so sparkling that it was a joy to read them aloud. And this had been achieved by a miracle.

Babel has himself told the story of how a certain young writer, who happens to be living penniless in St. Petersburg, and on false papers, helps a wealthy lady admirer of Maupassant to translate "Miss Harriet." In her clumsy translation, "there was nothing left of Maupassant's free-flowing sentences with their long breath of passion"; and the young writer "cut clearings all night long in this other person's translation."*

"This kind of work is not as awful as it seems," Babel wrote. "When a sentence is born, it is good and bad at the same time. The secret is to give it the right twist—a scarcely perceptible one. The lever must rest in your hand and get warm. Then you must turn it the right way—only once, not twice."

This passage from Babel's story has often been quoted, but I cannot refrain from repeating it here, because nobody has surpassed Babel's description of the knack of turning a poor sentence into a good one. [. . .]

Five or six changes on each page (and small ones, at that)— that was all Babel had done to these stories of his protegé's. And a page on which there had been nothing to hold one's attention, a page that was like a plain one wanders over,

---

* The story referred to is "Guy de Maupassant," first published in June 1932.

hoping to get to the end as quickly as possible, had become as picturesque as a path through a forest that constantly rewards the traveler with new impressions. I would not have thought it possible if I hadn't seen it with my own eyes. [. . .]

We once described this miracle wrought by Babel to one of our authors, Mikhail Yulyevich Levidov, a friend of the magazine, who was the biographer of Swift and an admirer of Bernard Shaw, and who published in *The Banner* mordant literary criticism and articles on international affairs. After hearing what we had to say and running his eye over the proofs of the story in question, Levidov burst out laughing. "Don't you see?" he said. "I mean, why Babel took such an interest in this 'budding writer,' as he called him?"

We looked at one another blankly. "Is it really important why he was interested?" one of us asked.

"Of course it's not important," Levidov agreed. "I know the most interesting thing about it is the miracle performed by Babel. But still, you must know that for a long time he has been a passionate fan of the races. And the author of these stories, judging by your description and the internal evidence of his work, is a jockey." [. . .]

Not long after, I had the good fortune to be present at a talk Babel gave for young writers. It was held in the conference room of the Union of Soviet Writers, and we all sat around a huge table. [. . .] He spoke about various things that evening, but particularly about how essential it is for a writer to have curiosity and the ability to be surprised, to see what is new and take pleasure in it. But it was what he had to say about Tolstoy which seemed to me most important. I wrote it down and I can repeat it now more or less verbatim.

"I was very surprised," Babel said, "when I learned that Tolstoy weighed only three and a half poods. But then I realized that it was three and a half poods of pure literature."

"What do you mean by that?" asked somebody sitting at the table. I don't believe Babel heard the question. In any case, what he went on to say did not sound like an answer.

"Reading Tolstoy," he said slowly and thoughfully, "I always have the feeling that the world is writing through him. You understand what I mean? His books convey the feeling that the existence of a great number of the most varied people— and not only people, but animals, plants, clouds, mountains, and constellations—has been poured out on paper through him. How can I put this more clearly? . . . You know what a 'conductor' is in physics, and about the resistance a conductor offers the electric current flowing through it. Well, as in electricity, there are writers who are almost ideal 'conductors.' Tolstoy was an ideal conductor because he consisted entirely of pure literature. It's wrong to think that talent for writing is a matter of being able to rhyme or think up abstruse, startling epithets and metaphors. That used to be my trouble, and I still have to squash these metaphors in what I write, just as some not very clean people squash the vermin they find on themselves. And this is why I say to you: avoid as much as you can indirect, refracted modes of expression, and the temptation to show off that way! Superior craftsmanship is the art of making your writing as unobtrusive as possible. When Tolstoy wrote, 'During dessert they announced that the horses were ready,' he was not concerned about the structure of the sentence, or rather he was concerned that the reader should give no thought to its structure. Or take a man who runs out into the street shouting 'Fire!' Does he think about how he should pronounce the word? He doesn't have to. The sense of the message is such that it will reach everybody, whatever its form. So let everything you wish to tell the reader have this kind of urgency. In your search for the best way to express your ideas, always be guided by Pushkin's golden words: 'Precision and brevity are the prime qualities of prose.' "

Babel paused and suddenly, with a smile—he sometimes smiled in such a way that, looking at him, you felt you were warming yourself by a fire—added: "Only, don't think it's all that easy, precision and brevity. That's the most difficult thing, much more difficult than writing beautifully. . . ." [. . .]

KONSTANTIN PAUSTOVSKY

A Few Words about Babel*

❁

O NE ALWAYS has great faith in first impressions. They are generally thought to be infallible. We always feel that however many times we might change our mind about somebody, we shall eventually return to our first impression of him.

The reason for this faith in first impressions must be that we are convinced of our shrewdness in sizing people up. In my own life I have often tested out these first impressions, and they have not always held up. A first impression is very tricky.

There were some puzzles and surprises about my first meeting with Babel, which took place in 1925 in Odessa, in the suburb known as Middle Fountain. This is part of the area west of Odessa that runs along the open sea: a stretch of land with old gardens and *dachas* called the Fountains ("Little Fountain," "Middle Fountain," "Big Fountain"), although there aren't any fountains there and probably never were. In typical Odessa fashion, *dachas* in the Fountains were elegantly styled "villas": Valtukh's villa, Gonnaryuk's villa, Izzy Krapotnitsky's villa, and so on. The Fountains were divided along their length into sixteen "stops"—after the number of trolley-car stops. These "stops" were all pretty much the same, with their

---

* *Neskolko slov o Babele: Memuary,* first published in the Moscow Sunday newspaper *The Week* (*Nedelya*), No. 11–17, September 1966.

gardens, *dachas,* steep paths down to the sea, broom bushes, and broken-down fences. The only thing that varied was the smells and the quality of the air. At the first stop, a dry odor of rank goosefoot and tomato plants came through the trolley-car windows. This was because the first stop was still at the edge of the city, within the belt of vegetable gardens and fields that encircled it. Here, in the dusty grass, gleamed a myriad pieces of broken glass, like thousands of toy suns. Particularly beautiful, glittering like emeralds, were the broken beer bottles. With every kilometer the trolley got farther from the outskirts of the city and closer to the sea, until at the ninth stop you could hear the roar of the breakers. Before long, the air was permeated with this roar and with the smell of cliffs bathed by the sea and drying in the sun, along with the sweet smell of mackerel being fried on pieces of sheet iron stripped off the roofs of abandoned *dachas* and sheds. But after the sixteenth stop, the air suddenly changed: it lost its pale, washed-out quality and became dense and deep blue. This dark blue air ceaselessly drove roaring waves onto the sands of Big Fountain, all the way from the shores of Anatolia.

I had rented a room with a veranda that summer in a boarded-up *dacha* at the ninth stop. Our neighbors across the road were Babel, his beautiful, red-haired wife Yevgenia Borisovna, and his sister Mary—Marykins, as everybody fondly called her.

Mary was extraordinarily like her brother and obediently carried out all the tasks he set her. These were many and varied, from transcribing his manuscripts on a rickety typewriter, to warding off the admirers, male and female, who pestered him. Already at that time they came out from town in droves to "get a look at Babel," and they got terribly on his nerves.

Babel had recently come back from the Red Cavalry, where

he had served as a simple private under the name Lyutov.*
His stories were already appearing in many magazines, in the
local *Chronicle,* in *Left Front of Art* (*Lef*), in *Red Virgin Soil,*
and in the Odessa newspapers. He was pursued by all the
young, literary men-about-town of Odessa. They annoyed him
no less than his female admirers.

He now walked hand in hand with fame. In our eyes he
was a grand old man of literature and a sharp-tongued sage
whose words brooked no contradiction.

Sometimes Babel invited me over for dinner. We all helped
lug a huge aluminum caldron of thin *kasha* up on the table:
"Come on now, all together!" Babel had dubbed this caldron
the "patriarch," and every time it was brought in, his eyes
gleamed hungrily.

His eyes had this same greedy look when he read aloud to
me, on the beach, Kipling's verse or Herzen's *Past and
Thoughts,* or a story by the German writer Edschmid† "The
Duchess," which he had somehow got hold of. It was about
the medieval French poet François Villon, who was hanged
as a highwayman, and his tragic love for a duchess who had
become a nun.

Apart from this, Babel loved to read Rimbaud's poem
"*Bateau ivre*," which he did magnificently, in French. He read
with great vigor and fluency, as though immersing me in its
whimsical style and in the equally whimsical flow of images
and similes.

"Incidentally," Babel said once, "Rimbaud was not only a
poet but an adventurer as well. He traded in elephants' tusks in
Abyssinia and died of elephantiasis. He had something in
common with Kipling."

---

* Lyutov is the name given to the narrator-protagonist of Babel's Red
Cavalry stories.
† Kasimir Edschmid (1890–   ), Expressionist writer popular in
Germany at the time.

"What was it?" I asked.

Babel didn't reply at once. Sitting on the hot sand, he was throwing flat pebbles into the water. Playing ducks and drakes was our favorite pastime: we liked to see who could throw farthest, and we liked to hear the pebbles plopping into the sea with the sound of champagne bottles being uncorked.

"*Satirikon*," said Babel, without relevance to what had gone before, "has been publishing the very gifted satirical poet, Sasha Chorny."*

"I know the sort of thing: 'Aron Farfurnik caught his only daughter and heir with the scatter-brained student Epstein.' "

"No, it's not all like that! Some of his verse is very sad and simple: 'Even though they are no longer, once they existed on earth, Beethoven and Heine, Pushkin and Grieg.' His real name was Glückberg. We've been throwing pebbles into the sea; one of his poems goes, 'There are also isles of lonely thought. Be brave and do not fear to rest on them. Here gloomy cliffs tower over the sea—one can brood and throw pebbles into the water.' "

I looked at Babel. He was smiling a sad, bemused smile. "He was a quiet Jew," he went on. "I was like that once, before I began to write and learned that quiet and timidity are no good in literature. You have to have strong fingers and whip-cord nerves to be able to rip out of your drab prose, until it bleeds, those bits you happen to like most but which are needed least. It's like self-inflicted torture. Why did I get into this hellish writing business? I just don't understand it. I could have gone into agricultural machinery, like my father— McCormick threshers and winnowers, and so on. Have you ever seen them? Real beauties they are, with all that smart, nice-smelling paint. You can almost hear the dry wheat rustling like silk through the fans of the winnowing machines . . .

---

* Sasha Chorny was the pseudonym of Alexander Mikhailovich Glückberg (1880–1933), who had left the Soviet Union in 1920.

But instead, I enrolled in the Psycho-Neurological Institute—
just so I could live in Leningrad and churn out my stories.
Writing! I've got asthma and I can't even shout properly, but
a writer can't mumble—he has to shout at the top of his voice.
You can bet Mayakovsky didn't mumble, and then there was
Lermontov, slamming his verse into our faces, us descendants
of those forebears renowned for their vileness . . .

"I learned only much later how Sasha Chorny died. He'd
been living in Provence, in a little town at the foot of the Alpes
Maritimes, a good way from the sea; you could just see it in
the distance, like a hazy blue abyss. The town was hemmed in
on all sides by a forest of Mediterranean pines—so fragrant,
resinous, and torrid. Hundreds of people with heart or lung
diseases would go to those woods to breathe in the healing,
scented air. And people who, according to the doctors, had
only two years to live went on for many more years after that.

"Sasha Chorny lived a quiet life, pottering about in his tiny
garden, delighting in the hot rustle of the pines when the wind
blew in from the sea—over from Corsica, no doubt. One day
some careless, or rather criminal, person dropped a lighted
match and the forest around the town went up in smoke and
flame. Sasha Chorny was the first to rush to try and put out
the fire. He was followed by the whole population. The fire
was put out, but a few hours later Sasha Chorny died in the
local hospital from heart failure."

It is difficult for me to write about Babel. Many years have
gone by since our first meeting in Middle Fountain, but I still
remember him as he seemed to me then—someone very so-
phisticated, who saw and understood everything. This always
inhibited me during my meetings with him. I felt like a small
boy; I was a little scared of his laughing eyes and his devastat-
ing quips. Only once in my life did I pluck up enough courage

to ask him to look at a manuscript of mine: "The Dust of Farsistan." Thanks to Babel, I had to write this story twice, since he lost my only copy. (Ever since then I have made it a habit, on finishing a new book, to destroy the draft after typing up a fresh copy. Only then do I have the feeling that the book is really finished, a blissful feeling which, alas, never lasts more than a few hours.)

In despair, I began to write this story again from the beginning. Almost on the very day I finished it—it was a difficult and thankless task—Babel found my original manuscript. He brought it back to me, but far from showing signs of guilt, he behaved like the injured party. He said that the only good thing about the story was the restrained passion with which it was written. But then he pointed out the purple passages in Oriental style—"Turkish delight," as he called them—and after that he told me off for misquoting Yesenin: "Some of Yesenin's words are enough to make your heart bleed," he said angrily. "You cannot be so careless with the words of a poet, if you regard yourself as a writer."

Another reason why it is difficult for me to write about Babel is that I have already said a great deal about him in my autobiographical works.* I keep thinking that I have said all there is to say, but this, of course, is not so. I am always remembering other things he said, or more details about his life.

I read his first stories in manuscript. I was struck by the fact that though he used the same words as other writers, they seemed to become more full-bodied, vivid, and graphic under Babel's pen. His language struck, or rather captivated, with its extraordinary freshness and concision. This man saw and heard life with an originality we were incapable of.

Babel always spoke with contempt about wordiness. Any

---

* For other Paustovsky writings on Babel, see his *Years of Hope* (New York: Pantheon Books, 1969), pp. 118–150. Also, in *New World*, No. 10, 1963, his memoir, *Book of Wanderings* (*Kniga skitanii*), which has not yet been translated.

unnecessary word in a piece of prose made him feel outright physical disgust. He crossed out unneeded words with such fury that his pencil tore the paper. He hardly ever said "I am writing," but rather, "I am composing." At the same time he would complain of his lack of writing ability, of imagination, which, in his words, was "the god of prose and poetry."

But however close to life, and even naturalistic, Babel's descriptions of his characters and their setting, the specifically "Babelesque" world he creates is a somewhat distorted one, sometimes an almost incredible, even anecdotal one. He could turn an anecdote into a masterpiece.

He once or twice cried out, irritated with himself: "What holds my things together? What sort of cement? They really should fall apart at the slightest touch. Sometimes in the morning I start to write about a small thing of no importance, some trifling detail or other, and by evening it's turned into an elaborate tale."

He answered his own question by saying that his stories were held together by their style only, but then he would laugh at himself: "Who's going to believe that a story can be made just by style—without content, or plot, or suspense? What sheer nonsense."

He wrote slowly and always put off handing in his manuscripts. He lived in a constant panic at the thought of words that could no longer be altered, and he was always trying to gain time—just a few more days, or even hours—so that he could sit over his manuscript a little longer and go on polishing, with no one pressing him or getting in his way. He would resort to anything—deceit, or hiding in some incredibly dreary place—just to stay out of people's way. At one time he lived in Zagorsk, near Moscow. He didn't give anyone the address, and one could see him only after complicated negotiations with Mary. Once, however, he asked me to go out there to see him. He suspected that one of his editors might suddenly turn up that same day, and he took me off to an abandoned refuge that had once been inhabited by hermit monks. We sat it out there until all the "dangerous" trains, the ones the editor could have taken from Moscow, had gone. Babel swore and cursed about all the callous, unthinking people who wouldn't let him work. Then he sent me out to reconnoiter, to see whether the coast was clear. But there was still some danger that the editor might turn up, and we went on sitting in the refuge for a very long time, until the dark blue twilight.

I had always thought of Babel as a true Southerner, a native of the Black Sea coast and Odessa, and I was secretly surprised when he said that dusk in central Russia was the best time of day, the translucent "witching hour" when the almost imperceptible shadows of branches appear in the gentle air and when a sickle moon rises suddenly above the edge of a forest, and sometimes far away you hear the sound of a huntsman's gun. "For some reason," Babel observed, "the sound of a gun in the evening always seems a very long way away."

Then we started talking about Leskov. Babel recalled that Blok's estate, Shakhmatovo, had not been far from Zagorsk, and he called Blok "an enchanted wanderer." I was very pleased by this. I thought the description fit Blok wonderfully well. He had come to us from an enchanted country far away and had led us back to it—into the nightingales' gardens of his sad and brilliant poetry. *

It was already obvious, even to someone unversed in literature, that Babel had come into it as a conqueror, as a first-rate craftsman with something quite new to say. If nothing were to

---

* Nikolai Leskov (1831–1895) wrote a novella called *The Enchanted Wanderer*.

Zagorsk, about 45 miles from Moscow, is the site of many famous monasteries and a place of pilgrimage.

Blok is, of course, the poet Alexander Blok (1880–1921). "Nightingales' gardens" refers to his poem of that title.

survive for posterity except his two stories "Salt" and "Gedali," this would be sufficient testimony that the advance of Russian literature toward perfection was just as steady as in the days of Tolstoy, Chekhov, and Gorky. By every sign and token—even, as Bagritsky° would have said, "by the way his heart beat"—Babel was a writer of enormous and generous gifts.

At the beginning of this article I spoke of one's first impression of Babel. From a first impression, one could never have told that he was a writer. He had none of the standard marks of a writer: he was nothing much to look at, there was not the slightest effort to strike poses or to give utterance to profound thoughts. The writer in him was betrayed only by his eyes, sharp and penetrating, which seemed to go right through you, laughing, both shy and mocking at the same time. He was also given away by the restless, silent sadness into which he sank from time to time.

We have to thank Gorky for Babel's rapid and sovereign entry into our literature. In return, Babel looked up to Gorky with reverence and love, as a son might look up to his father.

. . . Nearly every writer is launched on his career by some older comrade. I feel—and with good reason—that it was Isaac Emmanuelovich Babel, among others, who launched me, and so until my dying hour I shall always think of him with love, friendship, gratitude, and admiration for his talent.

° Bagritsky was the pseudonym of Eduard G. Dzyubin (1895–1934), a Russian-Jewish poet born in Odessa.

Ju
F
B31   Bat-Ami, Miriam.
b   Dear Elijah.

DATE	ISSUED TO